If you have ever longed to fly through the pure blue of the heavens,

or to ride through the fields on a magnificent steed, and wade through brooks as icy as fear,

or to know animals as they truly are, and meet people who can tell you so much you have never known,

if, in short, you want to enter T.H. White's own very special world,

you are about to open the door of enchantment...

ENGLAND HAVE MY BONES

T.H. WHITE, one of the world's most popular and beloved writers, is the author of the hugely successful THE ONCE AND FUTURE KING and LETTERS TO A FRIEND as well as many other entrancing works that magically mingle reality and the imagination.

T.H. WHITE
ENGLAND
HAVE MY BONES

'God keep my soul
And England have my bones'

BERKLEY BOOKS, NEW YORK

PREFACE

FEW people are interested in things, except the mechanics who like engines. They are more interested in themselves, and humanity, and theories, and emotions. I suppose quite a large percentage of people would not be able to name a grain of wheat from a grain of oats, or perhaps even a blackbird from a rook. Our ancestors of the nineteenth century grew up with things, so that they were real to them and had a sort of comfortable companionship now lost. That is why their things are so often more individual than ours. An old hobby-horse, turned up in an attic, will sometimes be so real that it is a piece of art, and clamours to be put on show in the hall downstairs. Not so the mass-produced Dobbin of to-day.

This book cannot pretend to be written by a naturalist, and it is not for naturalists. It is a book about things, for people who have lost them; because it has given me pleasure to rediscover my things, and I should like to shew them to other people who might be pleased as well.

It has turned into a book about the tangible side of country life. People, I felt, ought to pay more attention to the temperature of their baths, and the way they fill their pipes, and the birds who are squandering their song for a chance audience, and the spectacles of nature that give food for the pleasures of rumination, and the construction of fires, and the time to drink sherry, and the season at which a hot water bottle improves upon the comfort of warming one's own bed. In fact, it is an empirical book, an effort to return to the various world. Sport is a good way of doing that.

At the same time, I am sorry to feel that it must be a book which requires apology, or at least explanation. Fishermen will be maddened by the flying, aviators by the snakes, zoologists by the instructions for playing darts. It may seem a fair criticism to say that too many things are done, and none of them expertly. I find it difficult to imagine the kind of person who will bear with every digression. If there is such a person, he will be an amateur like myself: a reader with a forgiving mind, not a critical one: somebody not fascinated by sherry parties, who can see the point of an England defined by negatives. My England is not that of the *Saturday Review*, nor is it authoritative, like that of the *Field*. It is not stately enough for *Country Life*, nor experienced enough to bear comparison with the works of A. G. Street or Adrian Bell. I hope it is not the kind of country that is inhabited by Mr. Beverley Nichols.

It is, unfortunately, the country of a leisured class, and for that reason it tends to be unreal. This sense of unreality, which affects every sporting writer in the post-war world, lies at the back of all efforts to return to harmony with the genuine countryman. It is what makes my book digressional, kills it as a purely sportin' compilation without assuring it of any permanent reality. It made me learn to milk and plough: but always as an enthusiastic dilettante, always a little pathetically clamouring *outside* the gates of farming England.

I pretend to myself that the disability has brought a compensating joy. It is the book of a learner, at any rate. And I have a passion for learning. I have enjoyed learning to milk, and I enjoy to do it. My hands smell of milk as I write this; and my pen, now that the subject has been raised, rushes forward irresistibly to describe the milkman's ardours.

Cows, my inadequacy as a farmer urges me to explain, give better if sung to. The cow-house is warm and smelly, the milk hypnotic. It sizzles and rings in the pail. Down at the other end, friendly, simple, and English, the boy is roughly teaching a very young calf to drink from the pail (by using his finger in a bucket of milk like a tit) and old Matthew, so trustfully drunk at Shireham fair last Saturday, is singing a four-year-old fox-trot to the strawberry roan, as if we were in Bethlehem.

ENGLAND HAVE MY BONES

The English are serious. . . . They are good sailors and better pirates, cunning, treacherous and thievish; above three hundred are said to be hanged annually at London. . . . Hawking is the general sport of the gentry; they are more polite in eating than the French, devouring less bread, but more meat, which they roast to perfection. . . . They are powerful in the field, successful against their enemies, impatient of anything like slavery; vastly fond of great noises that fill the ear, such as the firing of cannon, drums, and the ringing of bells, so that it is common for a number of them, that have got a glass in their heads, to go up into some belfry, and ring the bells for hours together for the sake of exercise. If they see a foreigner very well made, or particularly handsome, they will say: 'It is a pity he is not an Englishman!'

A GERMAN VISITOR
(in 1598).

3. iii. xxxiv.

An essential of a man's life, if he wishes to rediscover a contact with the world outside him, is not mobility, but position. It is helpful, in a world whose values change so quickly, to be able to say, 'I am an Englishman.' I only mean this as a kind of identification, not for jingoism. When I was a small boy at school, I used to write my name in my school books, and then my school, and the town it was near, and the county it was in: followed in due order by 'England, Great Britain, Europe, the Northern Hemisphere, the World, Space.' I never got so far as writing 'Time,' though I should dearly have liked an additional category. I did this for remote and curious reasons: everybody else did. But I wonder whether in a way I was not trying to identify myself. Red Indians, I believe, are unsure of the distinction between themselves and the outside world. They find difficulty in being certain whether *it* is raining or *they* are spitting. I understand that most races were like this, in the youth of the world, and I am sure that children are like it still. When Weg falls down I expect she resents the world for falling up, and I can perfectly remember wanting to break a golf club because I was unable to hit a ball with it.

The small boy who scrabbled all that rigmarole in Kennedy's Eating Brimer was sorting himself out. He was saying, 'I am I, and I live here.' It seems to be a common tendency of human nature.

Nowadays we don't know where we live, or who we are. Intelligence seems to be merging again into the Red Indian void from which it sprang. The intellectual is physically helpless in a material world, and has to be looked after by servants, like those people in Swift. Even the non-intellectual tends to become totally vague about reality. He knows about the inside of his motor-car, and the relations of time tables, and sometimes the various co-ordinations of a tennis racquet; but all these things are artificial. He is fading into them, losing his identity in an abstract world where water is an idea that comes out of a tap, and light a conception in a switch. If all the main services failed, he 'would not know where he was.' The old phrase is appropriate.

This is why, in a shifting world, I want to know where I am. I want to find the things which won't fail with the services, to identify myself over again on a secure anchorage. I like staying in one place, so that I can learn it and let it grow about me as it is, instead of gadding from pillar to post in motor-cars and aeroplanes and trains. Moreover, when I stay in the country I am farther from the abstract tap-water: closer to the components which are most likely to endure in the world about my planted feet.

Therefore, as firmly as I ever was in Kennedy, I am an *Englishman*, and I live in the *shire*.

4. iii. xxxiv.

The Shire is a pasture country, about two-thirds sand, the rest clay and other components. It is well wooded, noticeable for its power of growing strong vegetation, so that it is sometimes referred to as 'lush.' There is scarcely any industry in it, and its people are gentle without being sleepy. Our nature is pitched about half-way between the doze of Norfolk and the fierce friendliness of Gloucestershire. We are not particularly associated with Oliver Cromwell, or Owen Glendower, or even William the Conqueror. The overbearing historical personages don't seem to have made us their playground very much; or if they did come, it was only in a hurry to get somewhere else. Poets, on the other hand, and particularly the more durable and less specacular of them, have found a safe harbour here without having to make a fuss about it. We were always more the country for monasteries than castles, and, since the monks were generally good landlords, we enjoy a peaceful agricultural tradition.

There is nothing remarkable about this county. We are hunted over by good packs of hounds, but they just fall short of the Osbaldeston-Sutton tradition. Our church architecture is respectable without being arresting. We are not obviously old-fashioned and not peculiarly new-fangled. We don't have much in the way of hills, and therefore very little in the way of valleys, nor are we entirely a question of vale. In fact, we live along.

Our county is a place. We don't stay in it all the time, but we do stay in it most of the time, and so we know it. When anything exciting happens in it, and we are so far from extremes that occasionally something does happen, we remember the occurrence for four or five hundred years. My small rough shoot is poached by the inhabitants of a village who do so because they have not forgotten that one of their villagers was hanged for poaching, a little less than two hundred years ago. Tom Bourne, who allows me to shoot over his farm, still calls an unfenced area in a grass field 'the Nunnery,' though there is not a brick or a stone left to mark the spot where the holy chapel once stood.

To put it shortly, we are residential. The locality has its roots so deep in a *peaceful* kind of time that it is enduring; it conveys a sort of stability to its residents; it is home.

6. iii. xxxiv.

One can't say that the Shire is a better place than anywhere else. Among other things, the place itself would scarcely appreciate the compliment. It would be against its nature to compete: it would lose what reality it possesses if it were made in any way to outstand. There are certain

counties which once had outstanding qualities, and which
have been overwhelmed for that reason. Sussex and
Devonshire are cases in point. Downs, Devonshire cream,
and damned bad literature, have provoked the invaders.
No sensible man can go to either of those places now.
Gloucestershire and Wiltshire are outstanding counties,
and play more strongly and instantly on the emotions than
does the Shire. But their loveliness makes them
provocative, and their day will come. The invaders will
top the skyline, marching under petrol pumps and curiosity shops and corrugated iron roofs. Gloucestershire,
whose architecture grows out of the earth, because it
builds with the stone it stands on, will blossom with red
brick and blue slates. Wiltshire, whose downs enclose the
fertile valleys, will bloom with loop-ways and mustard-
yellow touring signs and gentlemen from the A.A.

The Shire has protected itself against these things by a
non-committal policy. It makes no Banbury cakes or
Yorkshire teas or Devonshire creams. It has concealed its
individuality in order to preserve it. We have a few loop-
ways, a few yellow signs, a few corrugated iron roofs, a
few thatched ones, nothing very definite: so that the
invaders pass through, as Oliver Cromwell did before
them, looking for somewhere else.

10. iii. xxxiv.

There is no need even to be enthusiastic about the
county, and no compulsion to remain. I don't myself
consider it beautiful. The land prefers to make no demands
upon its inhabitants, but to exist as a position on the map
of England, for those who want it. A non-committal
earth, secretly exuberant in its private way, the Shire has
no reproaches for me if I go to fish in Scotland or, in the
summer, to look for another love. If I stay, the land is there
for me, with its Southdown, Oxford Down and cross-
bred Leicesters cropping the lush grass: if I go, I shall have

gone with Oliver Cromwell; but the Shire is still a position.

20. iii. xxxiv.

So is the whole British Island an anchorage, if you avoid the towns. So are birds and beasts and the sporting seasons. It would be possible to throw out other grapples. All the *things* which will outlast London are important to the philosophic man. The incredible swarm of the Wen, whose money-makers not only scramble over the surface of the nest in buses and on their feet, but also dive into it like maggots and pop up again at the exits of other tube stations, ceaselessly bustling about their carrion errands: all this swarm is impermanent beside the salmon. When London Bridge has tumbled down, and the sewers of the hive have ceased to pollute the waters, there will be salmon opposite the Imperial Chemicals building, but no Imperial Chemicals building opposite the salmon.

26. iii. xxxiv.

At Southam brook, beyond Leckley, a stream that you can jump on a horse, I caught the first trout of this year: ½-lb., in good condition. He was taken on a worm and eaten for dinner, as a charm to increase virility during the coming season. I awarded myself the title of Primoraro-tructicaptor, or Hammer of the Salmonidæ.

People who don't fish regard fishermen as crazy, or at least as if they belonged to another race: like monkeys or clergymen. 'How you can have the patience!' they say. It doesn't make me feel cross, but impotent, as if I were talking about logarithms to a Zulu. They have not experienced, and therefore need not believe in, other people's joys. It is the same with ghosts. Such people can't understand that the fisherman lives not patiently, but so far behindhand with what he wants to do, that the *rush* of

fishing obliterates time, and the day is over before he has
begun. They confuse him with the float-fisher, not realis-
ing that the skilful timing of a cast is as difficult as the
timing of a cricket stroke. Perhaps they don't even know
that half the true fishermen in the world are so excited
when they rise a fish that in striking him, if he is small,
they jerk him out of the water. So shattering is the excitement of getting into a fish, so violently does the heart leap
into the gullet, that I should put the 'patient' fisherman's
blood-pressure at treble the height of the hunting man's,
and five times that, for the very smallest fish, of the man
who kills a snipe.

Perhaps you do have to be patient in order to play the
abstract game of cricket; but when you wed the timing of
every stroke to the possibility of a kind of *living* 'six,' that
goes on fighting you for five minutes in still water, then it
becomes a little difficult to talk about 'patience' patiently.

6. iv. xxxiv.

The hunting season ends with a feeling of regret in the
Shire, especially if the last day is a fair one. To-day was
only moderate; but it suited a slow horse, and there was
jumping to be had if wanted. It was nice to be among the
dozen that didn't get lost when we ran to ground by the
Doric Bridge, having brought him from Weston Wild. It
was nicer to smash an enemy's lock at a gate: and to jump
one's own places: and so on. Two foxes were killed, but
they were headed in every direction. I stayed to the bitter
end, in sleet, and went home sadly to my bath. A bad
season for me, but I have been happy. Next winter will be
grand, but I shall be a year older. These thoughts were not
cheered by the spectacle of a growing stomach. Three
poached eggs restored confidence. The Rothmore on the
16th!

10. iv. xxxiv.

I have lived long enough in the Shire to be able to afford to go away from it with pleasure. I suppose this is what homes are for. If one hadn't got an anchorage it wouldn't be exciting to sail away. For a month now I have been turning over fishing stocks, reading books, looking forward to the opportunity of the first salmon of my life. A set of brand new salmon lures, Bulldog and Kessler's Fancy, have been sharpened all over again with a carborundum; thereby making them rather blunter than they were before. A dozen wet-fly casts for trout have been tied in advance: silver march brown, skinnum, butcher. No really decent-minded fisherman can avoid buying a few bright flies, useless except for sea-trout, if any use for them: and, once bought, he has to put up one or two of these for the ordinary trout, just in case, because they are so beautiful. Then every fly in the box has to be sharpened, and the eyes cleaned of gut in cases where they were bitten off in a crisis last season. The line has to be dried (it is bone dry already) and greased: the reel has to be taken to bits out of mere restlessness: and of course one has got to practise casts.

No fisherman can be a good man.
                    BYRON

16. iv. xxxiv.

I drove up from Tenmere to Aberdeen yesterday in 13¼ hours, including stops for breakfast, lunch and tea, and many other breaks of a few minutes at bridges to look at the fishy water: less than eleven hours' driving, and a distance of 516 miles on the speedometer. I arrived in a hail storm, like Amundsen; bought the best room in the Caledonian Hotel; had two baths, and slept it off.

People ought to take more interest in baths and extravagance. Both must be indulged in sparingly, to be properly appreciated. If I live in a public-house for ten months, and shave in the kitchen, then Claridges becomes an excellent way of expressing myself for two days. The true voluptuary wears sackcloth nearly all the time, so that when he does put on his sheer silk pants he can get the full satisfaction out of rolling in the hay. It is the same with baths. If I am continually washing myself, quite apart from the dangerous and insanitary nature of the practice, I shall cease to appreciate it. The *thoughtful* bather, who has a bath once a fortnight, is the man who knows that a bath ought to be entered warm, and raised to hot after entry, in order to experience the ineffable warmness, wetness, nakedness, milkiness of the steamy relaxation, percolating between his hams, with the winter night outside. It is the horny-handed and the leather-legged who properly enjoys his rare ablutions. He is the man who uses five shillings' worth of bath-salts at a time, and loves it; while the poor pansy, eroded almost out of recognition by excessive water twice a day, though in the baths of Cleopatra, can hardly with any delight raise up the ghost of a rose.

To-day I bought stock at Sharpes, Alexander Martin's and another's: drove to Grantly and settled at the Stratheven Commercial: drove to Craigenkillie Castle and found Macdonald out to his traps: fished right up the river and back again to discover its geography. But it was a hopeless spate. When I got back to the castle at 7.45 Macdonald was waiting. He says the water has been out of order since Thursday, but should improve soon. We are to fish two of the pools to-morrow with minnow for salmon. I could follow Charles' map from the Linbane pool down to Upper Crombie, but after that it became confused. A roaring brown torrent all the way: a staircase of dun waves with back-drafts leaping uphill, a spectacle of Biscay.

17. *iv. xxxiv.*

It was a hellish day, but in some ways grand, because it was medieval. I shook off the dust of Grantly after breakfast and picked Macdonald up from Craigenkillie at 10.30. The water was improved. We drove to the Gordon Arms, a superb John Buchan sort of beer shop, and left a bag, after covenanting for £2 a week. We drove straight down the precipice to Linbane farm and started fishing the Mill Pool at noon. I pricked what was supposed to be a salmon and a 3-lb. trout almost at once, but Cheese's rod seemed not heavy enough to drive home the multiple hooks of a Devon minnow. We went over the pool twice, and then up the river. In the Crooked Pot I took the first fish, a trout of 17 ounces. We fished up through the Ardgalleys fruitlessly, then back to Linbane for lunch. After lunch at 3.30 I tried the Mill Pool for trout, using Silver March Brown, Skinnum, and a blue-silver-teal sort of sea-trout fly, in that order from tail fly to top dropper, on a 4x cast. In one hour I had eight more fish, two ¾ lb. and the rest going down to ½ lb., and put them all back, except one of the ¾ lb. for breakfast. All three of the flies were taken; though the

gaudy one only once, by a very small stupid fish. Then we
went back to minnow, but in vain. At seven o'clock we
tried to restart the car and found that it had blown up. At
seven-thirty we decided to walk back to Craigenkillie, and
did so by moonlight over the moors. Macdonald would
take me to the nearest garage in his motor bicycle. But that
wouldn't start either. So we went on walking. By nine
o'clock we had reached a garage. By eleven-fifteen, after
sufferings which defy description, I got to the beer shop,
in a car that would not do 15 m.p.h., without an overcoat,
but having had the pleasure of walking across half a dozen
moors in two overcoats, until I shed them; and then found
that the next two hours were to be spent standing still
beside the derelict Bentley. I got to the beer shop, and
found they had gone to bed. 'They' were a witch and a
semi-imbecile natural, apparently. This is a grand
country: the pubs 15 miles apart, garages 10, telephones 8.
The Bentley will cost a fortune to repair, but it doesn't
matter. In any case the witch will cut my throat at night,
and feast upon my heart. To-morrow, if not, I am to be at
Craigenkillie by 8.30, to fish the Catloupe.

Macdonald assures me that I can catch a salmon before I
go, but it doesn't seem real. What is a salmon like? The
idea of it looms over the fishing day; but it is only an idea,
like the water in an urban tap. I can't imagine it in relation
to myself.

18. iv. xxxiv.

There were two things wrong with to-day. I could not
help thinking about the cost of motor-cars. The wind was
in the east. We started at the Bath Pool with high hopes,
but things proved more and more unfriendly, until noon
found us both flogging the Mill Pool like maniacs, for
anything. The Ardgalleys and the Crooked Pot and the
Duke's Pool were fruitless. By 7.15 I had three trout, all of
9 ounces, and Macdonald (tactfully) one of six or seven

ounces. I kept one of them for my breakfast. The rest went
back. Sad as the day appears on paper, it was a very nice
one indeed. By one o'clock there had been two
goosanders, four oyster catchers, two teal and one sandpiper, beside the usual plover and partridge. The
goosanders looked rather like the oyster catchers, in their
marking, at any rate. And the oyster catchers made the
same sort of noise as the sandpiper. Macdonald puzzled me
by saying that the 'Guckoo' was late. The primaries of the
plover buckled to the wind on a turn, like the tawse of a
brogue. The pine clumps on the moors had dead trees in
them, like the badger bristles on a tramp's old chin. Then it
began to rain. It was a Homeric east-winderly rain, as
repeatedly described by the Southcotes. Just as my fingers
were turning into slippery, cold-storage fish, Macdonald
shouted that he had had a pull from a salmon. I hurriedly
buckled on a minnow and followed him down. Then he
put on a larger minnow and came down after me. In vain.
We lay under a bank and talked. The Brown Hill had white
whisps crawling over it. The snow on the higher moors
vanished in the storms. There was a rainbow right across
the arc, a perfect semicircle. Earlier on there had been a
minor rainbow which started at my feet. I never saw this
before. It went up beside my rod, and vanished to the left.
So it has been a lovely day, if not a good fishing one. Also
Macdonald taught me to throw a salmon fly, with his
14-ft. rod. I had three spells of five or ten minutes and
stopped with a good cast.

Back to the beer-house, in a hired car, for a splendid
high tea at 8.30. The food is excellent. The bread has a
mouldy taste, due to its not being mouldy – like the
chemical muck we have in England. Peat fires. The witch
and her brood are lovely. There are two texts in my
bedroom. Why do these people live, particularly the small
crofters? I ask Macdonald about them incessantly. They
have no amusements, only relaxation. When they are not
working they seem to sit in front of the fire, doing

nothing, reading nothing, and not speaking. No wonder they hang up texts and believe in the devil. Bare moors, few neighbours, a but and ben. Are they wildly religious or fiercely immoral? How do they get rid of themselves? No doubt they are warlocks in secret, but that I am not let into. My witch treats me like a strange animal.

The gravel is beginning to show in the burn: red. Granite, heather, peat ash. Why is rose to purple the national shade? Is Scotland rich in iron? Even the wrens.

19. iv. xxxiv.

I can't begin describing to-day. The rainbow last night was a good sign, and I woke up feeling that it was going to be a massacre. But the window was wet and the slate sky icy. Still, it might clear at noon. We started on the Mill Pool straight away, on the assumption that one never knew. There might be. And so we cast slowly down, and the east wind blew the rain through everything, and the river was higher still (it has not yet been in good condition) and the more we cast the more it grew upon us that hope was dead. From 8.30 till 1.15 we wandered on the banks, like lost souls staying for waftage. It didn't clear at noon. We tried the Crooked Pot; we tried the Ardgalleys; we tried up above the snipe marsh to the bitter end. I cracked off one of my two Kessler's Fancies. The east and watery wind blew Macdonald's casts on to the bank, to my secret joy. My mackintosh was torn at the back. I only had a cap, and that was a cold poultice. I wore it back to front, in the vain effort to keep the rain from running down my neck. I paid out a sticking line with slippery, frozen fingers: the horrible and slightly rasping stickiness of cold wet deer's fat. I snapped off one of Macdonald's flies, using the salmon rod, by catching it in the bank. I found it again, and tied on in an ague.

At 1.15 we had lunch. We didn't talk much. Macdonald says that witchcraft *was* practised about here, but it has

died out. There were three curlew and a thing like a black
water rat: probably a form of were-wolf.

From 1.45 to 2.30 we draggled miserably back towards
the Mill Pool. By now Macdonald was fishing in front
with the fly and I was coming after him, hand-lining a
minnow off Cheese's rod. It became really impossible to
go on. I couldn't feel the line. I forgot whether it was hail
then or sleet. I asked Macdonald if he would mind my
using his spinning rod. It was a case of wanting something
to do, but being unable to go on hand-lining. I had four
casts, and caught the bottom. By now I was accustomed to
this and didn't strike. At the sixth cast I caught it again, but
it was a little different. It just seemed to move: an inch, a
millimetre. I struck. It couldn't be what it seemed. The line
cut the water, not quite in the usual way. I could have felt, I
thought, I did feel that it was moving towards me. But I
was not going to tell Macdonald, not yet. It was a salmon.
Oh, God, it was a salmon, and it would obviously get off
at once. I pulled and waited and it was coming and it didn't
seem to get off. It was deep. It stayed deep.

I shouted to Macdonald, who came, thinking I was
snagged. I said: 'I think I have a fish.'

He looked at me to see if I was mad, then at the line to see
if he was. He said: 'You have. Yes, certainly you have.'
Then he began to become hysterical. If it had been his own
fish he wouldn't have minded. But he had been wanting
one for me for three days, and he was terrified I would lose
it. He was in agony because he said I was holding it too
hard. He beseeched me to let it go. I assured him that it was
quite all right. I talked conversationally about different
ways of killing salmon. I asked him to look at the time.

Then the fish came up for a second. Macdonald said: 'It's
a big trout,' and my heart went down.

I said: 'Thank God it isn't an eel.'

He said: 'But no trout would hold you down like that. It
would come up and flutter on the surface.'

It was only the reddish water, the aftermath of the spate,

which had made him look rusty. I played him. I was hard on him, except when he had to go. He only took me 20 yards down the bank. Macdonald kept pleading for kinder treatment, but I wouldn't. I didn't know how long it was going to go on, or what was likely to happen, but I was going to hold him tight. I became aware of the moment when the cast would snap supernaturally, and let him off at that moment.

I brought him up, and we could get a good look. He was lovely and terrible, like a shark. I knew we couldn't possibly have him. He sloughed in the water. Then he was weaker and came towards us. Then he was off. And then back slowly, but still too strong. Twice more, and he was swimming just below Macdonald. Macdonald slashed at him, and *missed*. I said, agonised, 'No hurry,' and took him off for another circular tour. At last he was floating on his side, exactly below the executioner. This time there was no mistake. The gaff pulled like lightning: he was on the bank!

My first salmon. 10½ pounds. 13 minutes.

Incredible, but killed. I stuffed a pound into Macdonald's pocket, against his will, nearly cried, and went on fishing. Occasionally I peeped at the salmon. For some reason I didn't like to give it a close look. It would have been a kind of hubris to look at it closely. It might have vanished.

Thinking back over this incredibly wonderful experience, the only time I shall ever kill my first salmon again, several things become vivid. There was the way he took me. I understand now what fishing writers mean by a 'determined pull.' There was no grab, like a trout's. He simply *took* hold of me, not *caught* hold, and held me down. It was as if I were a small boy that he was going to spank. It was a determined outrage on my minnow, nothing wild or flashy about it at all. Then there was the extraordinary and unforced calm which descended when I knew he was on. I felt happy and interested, as if I had been condemned to death. This changed once, when my line jammed on the handle of the reel. Then I said: 'Oh, it's jammed.' It was a lamenting squeal, and I heard my own voice. I also remember Macdonald saying: 'Well, if we can only get this one on the bank, we can call it a guid day.' The important thing was the weather. Just for that twenty minutes the wind veered west and the sun shone. It woke the salmon up and they began to move up once more. But before moving they felt lively and took. I am sure that I hooked this fish during the only three or four minutes when it would have been possible to take fish by any means. The sun went in again, the wind went east, the rain came down: but there was a silver cock salmon on the bank. The first from Craigenkillie this year.

When people talk about salmon here they call it 'a fish.' Trouts are just trouts. A fish means a salmon. Quite right.

20. iv. xxxiv.

The ways of God are strange. To-day the wind was in the west and there was no rain: nor were there any fish. Only trouts. I gave these a few moments, and took two of ½ lb., which went back, but salmon have got into my blood. The whole day's flogging by both of us brought nothing. Only, on one occasion, on the Upper Crombie, I *may* have had a pull. Macdonald says they were moving up. Perhaps the wind was too strong. In any case, the only notable thing was that I fell in. I behaved well. I sat in the torrent, holding the rod carefully above my head, and fished out the cast. Later on I found that I had smashed my fly box and my tin for gut, by falling on them. It was very wet. I am glad to have fallen into the Rothmore. It is the proper form, probably prescribed by the church: like baptism or the churching of women.

Nothing else of note in to-day's fishing, except that the following wind gave an exaggerated idea of my ability with a salmon rod and fly. I told Macdonald that I should die happy if I could catch three fish: one on the spinning rod, one on the salmon rod, and one on Cheese's. He said: 'Well, if you fish as well as you have fished this pool (the Bath Pool) I can see no reason why you shouldn't take a fish on the saumon rod, and when the water goes down, I can promise you one on the troot.' So much for a perfect, though blank day.

Non-fishing affairs are in a tangle. The only two so-called mechanics within hundreds of miles have been so busy mending the Bentley that it is now impossible to make it go at all. Also, I can no longer afford to hire cars to and from the Gordon Arms. So this morning I read my texts for the last time (the better one said: 'Christ is a kind master, Sin is a hard one, You cannot serve both, Which shall it be? As for me and my house, we will serve the Lord') and bid good-bye to the witch. I shall come up again in the summer holidays and fish her water. Apparently one can get about three miles, sleep all day and fish all night. I shall bathe. I said goodbye to the witch and removed to the post office at Edendalloch. The car is still at the Gart. The post office is horrible—coal fires, attempted English meals and every horror, all with the kindest intentions—but it is only 1¾ miles from the water and there is a bus once a day.

Falling in love is a desolating experience, but not when it is with a countryside. I am going to give up hunting; make and save money; leave the Shire; and buy Craigenkillie from Sir Peter's executors—after poisoning him, whatever the price. And I shall *live* there. All the spring and summer I shall fish and sing. In the early autumn, and till the very 12th of December, I shall shoot my moors. In the grand long winter nights I shall sit over a peat fire in the tower, practising witchcraft and tying flies. I have bought an ounce of tobacco called Warlock already. Then, when I am dead, they must bury me in a bend of the river, like Colonel Leslie. I have an odd and senseless desire not to be cremated. It would be much more sensible, dignified and pleasant for the mourners; but I want to be buried low down, in the nook of a salmon river. Then I shall be able to hear impalpably the whaup and the sandpiper, and the less lovely noise of the plover. The water can flood over me if it likes, and I can feel the big fish running up near, and I can rot and be fertile without upsetting people by draining down the hillsides. The cemeteries are in the lowest valleys. All this is not intelligent, but it is a grand feeling.

A grouse to-day said 'talk' as clearly as any pheasant ever said 'cock.'

The post office is hell. They have put me in a vast, over-furnished, best room, principally ornamented with tobacco-cosies made out of polished coconuts.

21. iv. xxxiv.

Emotion, according to Wordsworth, should be recollected in tranquillity: and the bitter, utter black dejection of to-day would probably be better left to another night for record. However, I prefer to get it done with. I was fishing by 7.30 in sunshine and westerly gale, and fished alone with the salmon rod and Bulldog till 1.30, when Macdonald joined up. He had been away to his traps in the morning. I fished well, in spite of the gale. Then we had lunch. At 2.15 we concluded that salmon were hopeless till evening, and determined to try two big trout which lay in the Ardgalleys. I fished them dry on 4x cast with a March Brown, and killed the first. He was 15½ inches, but only 1½ lbs. Bad condition. Pricked the second. Get him later. Sat and talked. At four we started again for salmon, fishing with Macdonald's rod, in turns. He did the Mill Pool, and flicked off two flies in the wind, again to my joy. Then he said that he really would prefer me to kill a fish, so I took the rod all the way down to Lang's Pot. By then my back was almost broken with the wind. I gave the rod to Macdonald and said: 'Just fish this water above the bridge, to give me a rest.' I went to cross the bridge, over a side burn, and had no sooner turned my back when there was a splash and a shout. Macdonald had been taken before even casting, whilst paying out line. I suppose there have been bitterer moments. I walked about behind him, on the verge of tears. He offered to let me run it, but I refused to touch his fish. Gaffed it for him, after missing, and it weighed 14 lbs. It had jumped twice. We put it in the bag, on my poor little trout. The Catloupe and the Bath were blank. My heart is in two pieces. One consolation: it was an absolutely perfect tragedy.

22. iv. xxxiv.

Sunday. Fishing illegal. I was woken at 4 a.m. by two blackbirds, singing like angels, and worked at another book. Now that some of yesterday's horror has worn off I can record a story of Macdonald's which amused me. It was about a short-sighted gentleman who was a bad fisherman, but he enjoyed it. Macdonald swears that he once fished the whole of the Mill Pool with his fly caught in the knee of his plus-fours. 'He could hear the line splashing into the water,' says Macdonald, 'and that keepit him happy.' 'But why didn't you tell him?' I asked. 'Ah,' says Macdonald, putting his finger by the side of his nose, ''twas safest there.'

The post office is still cosmopolitan, but it has a nice double bed. All the beds in Scotland seem to be double, and a good thing too. But they are too short. Mine has two pots that live underneath it, side by side and upside down. It is a cosy, connubial and egg-like relationship.

When I am the Laird of Craigenkillie, I propose to be a wicked laird. If not eating the children of my tenants in the shape of a were-wolf, I shall hunt the tenants themselves across the moors, with black mastiffs. It will make very little difference to them in any case: their life is already insupportable. I shall be ninety years old, my nose will meet my chin, and I shall hunt my hounds out of a bath-chair drawn by Shetland ponies. I shall have to wear a huntsman's cap, a plaid shawl, and an ear-trumpet: and I shall wave an ebony walking stick with silver knobs.

The small farmer who has the field opposite the Mill Pool ploughs it with a cow and a horse together. The bored and pansified gait with which the cow walks is indescribable.

This evening I felt a twinge for the Shire. Jimmy Warm is sitting over a fire in the tap-room of the Crown, whilst I am writing this. I must send him a small part of my bliss here, if I can: a salmon perhaps would do.

Space is an arbitrary division, as strange as time. The Crown is as near to me, if I choose to think of it, as the earliest history of the Shire is in time. I can be close to them, and write about them, even in Scotland: especially on a Scots Sunday. Thinking this, I fell to wanting to write about the Shire: about its many-leaved, thick-trunked presence, five hundred miles away; about the derivation of its name, nowadays considered unsound, from an ancient word which meant a 'beech'; about its various, unimportant little alumni—the saint who cherished a pet swan which now adorns the town hall, the other holy man who distinguished himself by putting the devil in a boot, the two Lollards who were burnt at Shireham, and the mysterious executioner of Charles the First. All these things, however, must wait until I am back at home: or for another dull, unfishable Sunday.

23. iv. xxxiv.

There was a good deal of rain yesterday, and the river was still high, but the wind was in the north-west and much moderated compared with that of Saturday. We were fishing by 7.30 again, and drew blank up to the Mill Pool. There I killed a small fish of 7 pounds, on the 13-ft. rod, with a Bulldog, in eight minutes. The Crooked Pot was blank. In the Lower Ardgalley I had a fish of nine pounds on the same lure, and killed him in ten minutes. He was more exciting to run here than in the simple waters of the Mill Pool. Both fish before 11.30. I had a pull in the pool above the Dukes (alleged by Charles to be 'no good,' but the contrary by Macdonald) and unfortunately it was nothing serious. I also had a trout of 11 oz. who was stupid enough to attack the Bulldog, but went back. From now on, the day went wrong. We lunched at the Mill Pool, after flogging it again, tried the Middle Ardgalley for my friend the second trout (and caught his fly-taster, who went back), worked our way homewards from four o'clock. The rain had set in. I had a pull in the Catloupe, but again only a tentative one, at 7.30, and stopped at 8.0 on a snowstorm. The Brown Hill looks beautifully salted.

A good day's sport. After Saturday's tragedy I don't encourage Macdonald to fish in front of me, and he, which is a grand sign, refuses to fish behind. So he fishes the water that I leave out. When I do the Crooked Pot, he does the Island Pool, and so on. He had no fish, and I am not a gomeril.

A good day in other ways besides this. I saw a heron, four redshanks and a kestrel. The fields opposite us lead a very full life of their own. On Saturday there was the cow, on Friday (which I haven't previously recorded) there were fifteen white hens and a cock walking along with the wind behind them and their tails over their heads, like a bustle of Victorian beauties at a boisterous Ascot, and to-day there was a plough horse that had fallen down and couldn't or wouldn't get up. The whole family of his owner (three men, one woman and two boys) stood round him, slapping him, pushing him, pulling him with ropes, and placing his hoofs in suitable positions for getting up. He may have been bewitched, and he may have been suffering from a nervous breakdown consequent upon the conditions of labour in this part of the country. But the stupid expression which he put on, and the fact that he got up perfectly easily when they had slapped him enough, point to another direction. I was watching from the other side of the river, and when he did get up I clapped. This made them all furious, except the boy, who was delighted.

Macdonald swears that a friend of his knew a ghillie at Aboyne. The ghillie was attending to a lady. She hooked a fish and had a thrilling struggle, which worked upon the nerves of the ghillie. He became wildly excited. Upon the fish making a dash straight at the rod, he was observed to rush backwards up the bank, beckoning meanwhile to the lady's hinder parts, and exclaiming: 'Airse this way, mum! Airse this way!'

My ankle is giving way again, and it took 35 minutes to walk back to the post office. But to-morrow, before the snow melts at noon and brings a spate, I propose to catch the fish who pulled me in the Catloupe, if I have to crawl. It will be the most exciting pool for a run in the whole river. Order of presentation: Kessler's Fancy (small), Bulldog (medium and large), Fly spoon, small blue minnow, medium silver minnow, Macdonald's gigantic minnow, gaff with hay tied round it. If none of these work I shall dive in and bite.

Macdonald described a heron fishing. It stands with its neck stretched right out, and its head on one side. Then it makes a dart. Tom Bourne in the Shire calls it something that sounds like Mollern—as if it were a corruption of Moll-heron. I am sorry to say that I once shot one of these beautiful creatures needlessly, not even in a fishing country. It was in the north of the Shire, where the ditches are as foul as the eels that live in them. I had been sent out to kill rabbits early in May, not for the pot nor even for the pleasure of a sporting shot, but because they were a menace to the young corn. I was to shoot them sitting: buck, young, or doe in kindle. It was butchery, but it was a job that had to be done like any other. I went out with the heavy gun on my arm and saw a heron almost at once. He was standing in the green fields, and attracted my eye as he got up: a great sweeping bird, trailing a sweeping shadow behind him. I marked him down in the little brook, and wondered whether I could get up to him. Herons are reasonably cunning, so I thought it would be good sport to try. I kept telling myself that I was not going to shoot at him, as he was a beautiful bird, useless to me, and doing no harm to anything I valued. Another part of me said it would like to shoot a heron. We skirted along the hedge by the ditch in a state of suspended debate, with the chances rather in favour of the heron's survival, and anyway with little expectation of getting up to him. We did get up to him. I had marked him down farther off than he actually was, and suddenly here he was bustling out of the ditch by my right hand, in a great flurry. I shot him mercilessly, with only enough law to slip the safety catch and change my finger to the choke. He came down flump, in a crumpling parachute of blue-grey feathers, and I was miserable at once. His neck, which he had been accustomed to carry in a more than swanlike Z whilst he was flying, now lay loose on the earth like a bit of slack rope thrown down. His grey eyelid slowly rose up and covered the black eye, with its bright yellow circle. His lemon yellow beak lay on its side, his cold legs were still wet from the brook, and the wind which he couldn't feel blew among the untidy spinsterish feathers of his back.

I had qualms to-day, after my second fish. Are fish really cold-blooded and more or less impervious to pain? If so, what brings them absolutely broken to the gaff? Not exertion, certainly, and if fear then it is little better. Not exertion, because the strain exercised by a rod is comparatively small. To test this, hold the fly in one hand and bend the rod to the normal running position. Hardly anything.* It is a bad thought that these lovely silver creatures are brought in, killed by an agony worse than toothache.

*But the weight of the fish in the water will be so much less than it is on and that perhaps this pull is in fact sufficient to tire.

I no longer want to have a fish on Cheese's trout rod, unless it gets there by bona fide accident on a trout fly. It would get boring after an hour or so, and it would prolong the agony of the fish. Anyway I shan't try on purpose. It would be silly.

24. iv. xxxiv.

Fishing by 8.30 in an easterly blizzard, alone. All the lures failed in the Catloupe and I wandered up to the Mill Pool in some sorrow, trying a minnow here and there on the way. The water was already slightly up and it rained continuously. Hand-lining the minnow (left on from the last attempt at my friend in the Catloupe) was bitter work. Fished the Mill Pool with fly and then with minnow. I went back to fly at the Crooked Pot (all this meant casting in the teeth of the east wind) and reached the Lower Ardgalley just before noon. The sixth cast had him, undeservedly, on a bellying line, at precisely twelve o'clock. I had naturally left the gaff at the Crooked Pot, being far too wet and frozen to expect a fish. I was alone.

Well, it was a grand run. I had to take him over the rapids, back to the Crooked Pot, which was fortunately downstream, and to cross a foot-bridge myself in the process. Not knowing the snags in the river well, I was in agony all the way over the rapids, piloting him between stones with frantic care. When we got there he was still on, and as I picked up the gaff Macdonald hove over the horizon. But I was not going to be cheated of the full laurels at this stage. At exactly ten minutes past twelve I gaffed him out by myself, and he was 12¾ lbs. The fly was the Bulldog, on the 13-ft. rod and light salmon cast.

We re-fished all the Ardgalleys, and the Crooked Pot, and the Mill Pool, both fly and minnow, whilst the weather became steadily more arctic. Then lunch, wrapped in coats and mackintoshes, with the rain down our necks. Then we did it all over again. Then we lay on the bank and became torpid, hibernating in the showers. At about five o'clock Macdonald shewed signs of wanting to go home. The river was several inches up and there seemed to be no prospects. I said I would come too, just throwing a quick fly over the Upper Crombie, Lang's Pot and the Catloupe. On the way down, the lambs were playing in the opposite fields: absolutely lovely: thirteen to fourteen of them charging up and down their special playground, whilst a Nannie sheep looked on like a nurse in a poem by Blake. They ran races, all together, butted each other, and occasionally made tentative attempts to mount. A brave new world, about a month old.

The Upper Crombie was in bad order and blank. When we reached Lang's Pot, Macdonald said: 'You fish the top end with the fly and I'll fish the bottom with a minnow: then we'll have two fish.' I thought to myself: 'It'll be odd if we do get two,' and began. I think I deserved my fish. It was not a splash and a dash. I covered the whole surface without a blemish, and hooked him, striking with him, at about the twentieth cast, far out. For some reason he looked a monster, and the rod had evidently been weakened by my efforts in gaffing my own fish in the morning. I had scarcely looked at my watch and got up to the foot-bridge, when there was an ominous crack. The rod had been broken once before, rebound, and now was sprung. I lowered the pressure at once; and brought the fish to gaff in eight minutes, with one of the canes gone. Weight 10 lbs. only: fly again the Bulldog. This fly has now killed 38¾ lbs. of fish. If he tops the 40 I will retire him, and he shall live a life of ease and luxury in an envelope of transparent paper stuck to a page of this book.

After this triumph I stopped fishing, and, when Macdonald had covered the Catloupe, we came home.

If only there was a pub to go to, and English draught beer for my evening, this would be the most perfect day of my life. Walking back to the post office I passed a terribly crooked man, twisted into fantastic shapes by excessive

labour. It was past seven o'clock, but he was still topping
turnips. I thought how much happier than he I was, and
for no known reason. Of course the rational remedy for
this is communism: but then the rational remedy for the
agonies of the fish is to give up fishing. So much for
reason.

25. iv. xxxiv.

Salmon are as mysterious as everything else in my life. It
seems, however, to hold good that they prefer it cold in
spring. Apparently when the river rises they move up, and
when moving won't take. But, as with scent, there seem
to be a hundred other considerations. Yesterday the water
was an indigo slate, with the white scum standing out
against it vividly. The scum bubbles are supposed to be a
bad sign. Yet I had two fish. To-day the scum was just the
same, but I had none. It was a warmish day with big
bellying white clouds. Macdonald called it sultry: and it
was, when scrambling over the hillsides with a game
bag, rod, gaff, lunch basket, overcoat, mackintosh and
scarf. I fished alone till two o'clock. Then Macdonald
joined up, but we did nothing, though sticking at it till 9
p.m. I had one pull at 8.30, but so slight that there was no
touch at all. I merely saw the line tug, struck instantly, and
struck empty water. Over my very last beat I flicked off
the old campaigner of a Bulldog and lost him: a minor
tragedy. Still, perhaps he will be happier getting rusty in
the Scots heather than he would have been in a poky book
in the south.

As with yesterday, I did not take a trout rod, and was
rightly served out. There were half a dozen hatches of big
March Browns. They sailed down like Armadas, and the
trout went mad, butting at them shoulder to shoulder.

I am too sleepy to write more.

26. iv. xxxiv.

K.G. gets back from his Mediterranean tour, or whatever it was, on the 28th; and I want very badly to send him a diplomatic salmon. So the fishery has developed into a sordid race with time. Macdonald and I fished almost without stopping from 8 a.m. to 8 p.m., and in vain. It was an easterly blizzard with rain, sleet, etc. The east wind here is the one that brings rain. I never had a pull. Macdonald had a fish on for about six minutes, but it had taken the hook so gently as not to be appreciable until he began the back-draw for another cast, and the hook had lost its barb. He gave it its head for a second, and it was gone. He did not even swear.

To-day's object being solely to kill fish for K.G., I took Macdonald to the Mill Pool in the car (which is recovering) at eight o'clock, and came back myself to Craigenkillie. Then he fished to the top and back, whilst I fished up from the Castle. We met again at the Mill Pool and crossed over to each other's beats. We then repeated the process. I fished every pool in the river thoroughly twice, and some three or four times. Not a single pull. Added to this I lost my only other Bulldog, at once, whilst paying out line to begin the first pool. It stuck in a twig in midstream. The rest of the day was fished with an old fly of Olney's, tied round with silver paper out of a Goldflake packet and red thread unpicked from the laundry marks of my handkerchief: a Wills' Fancy, I shall call it.

The car is recovering because I have ignored it and waited for somebody to do something. The result is that a man has materialised from Bentley's and a new magneto and all sorts of other miracles. This comes of not being businesslike: a great blessing.

What adds excitement to the race against time is that the Craigenkillie record until May is seven fish. I have five to my rod, and Macdonald one, so there is a chance of holding a new world's title. Also a 25-lb. fish has been reported seen below at Edendalloch. Please God, let it be a salmon day to-morrow.

I caught a lamb, only a few days old. It was too cold, wet and miserable to notice me coming up behind. I just stroked and scratched the crisp curls on its little back, and then its mother frightened it by saying baa in an anxious voice. It got up and walked off, and its mother sniffed where my hand had been, giving me a cold look.

Remember the stone cheese-press in the deserted farm.

27. iv. xxxiv.

Please God, thank you for K.G.'s fish. We are now equal to that record between us, and I am one short of it to my own rod. Here is one of its scales.*

The day was identical with yesterday as regards the weather, only perhaps not quite so much rain. It was cold and rainless till about 10.30, though very windy from the east. I went straight up to the Mill Pool at about 9.15 and fished it as carefully as possible, with the wind. Nothing. Then I took the long straight stretch below the Island Pool, where Macdonald had his fish on yesterday. It gets a little protection from the east wind, and it is possible to fish it straighter. At the very bottom, just above the mound, I had a strong pull, struck, and had him on. He was there three or four seconds. Then the fly came back to me. (It was a Bulldog, by the way: I found that I had bought three after all.) I said audibly: 'O God! O Hell!' and put another cast in the same place. Macdonald says that a fish never comes again, but I seem to remember that Chaytor advocates a second attempt. Macdonald is a magnificent fisherman and I believed him, but I made the second cast in a wild attempt to relieve my own feelings. Nothing. I made a third cast, trembling with sorrow and indignation. And then he was there. I pressed on him hard,

*It would be pleasant, but impossible, to give one away with every copy.

in an agony of doubt for the first few seconds, in case he should go again. But he stayed there. He was lively and he leapt. I performed acrobatics to look at my watch. The gaff was fifty yards down the bank. He adopted a to-fro tactic across the river. As I am lame it was a struggle. There was a tussling limp back to the gaff, and the fever of taking the champagne cork off its point with one hand. It wouldn't have mattered so much, except for K.G. I brought him to gaff three times, and laid it along his side, but wouldn't strike till he was absolutely done in, for fear of bungling. He burrowed the bank with his nose, making me fear for the cast. As I was certain that he was Macdonald's fish, and therefore that he had twice got off the hook, and as I was still using the sprung rod, I did not cease to be terrified. In exactly nine minutes I lifted him cleanly out (the gaff going right round his spine), panted at him with amazement, and grabbed his tail to knock him on the head. He weighed 8½ lbs., a small fish, but good enough. The Bulldog is the finest spring fly that ever was seen.

The rest of the day was blank and the rain set in. The record is not beaten, and I have only two more fishing days.

A Major Wynne came over to fish to-day, and will be here on Saturday and Monday. Hence Macdonald's absence, ghillying him. I disliked him at sight and he is a rotten fisherman. He brought about a hundredweight of stuff, fished the Mill Pool with a minnow because he said it was too windy to get a fly across, and had two people trailing down the bank after him carrying his collection of gadgets. He was here so that he could talk about his fishin' later on. He treated Macdonald and his chauffeur abominably (actually handed the rod to Macdonald, for him to wind up the reel, when he had finished fishing a pool), came over *after* the morning take and left *before* the evening one. He has three rods on the Spey, and bucked about it. Enough of Wynne.

28. iv. xxxiv.

On account of the damnable Wynne (though he was not unpleasing to-day: people get nicer as you know them better) I spent the whole morning below Tammy's Burn. It seemed polite to leave him the first go of the best water up above. Naturally he didn't turn up till noon and went away before six, thus missing both takes. However, I left him the water. The Bentley is having its appendix out, so I had to catch the 7.10 bus, and was fishing by 7.30. I went right up to Tammy's Burn very carefully with the Bulldog, and back again, fishing all the odd corners, by half-past one. Like a fool I left out the Broad Pool, on a futile aversion that I harboured towards it. It has always been blank so far, and that was my only reason: a stupid one. Lunch in the gun-room over a fire. The first time I have had a dry lunch. The day, by the way, was identical with yesterday, only perhaps a little less wind: it is difficult to distinguish between a blizzard and a gale. After lunch I was staggering up towards Lang's Pot, with the intention of fishing it, when I saw the Blairglassie ghillie at it already from the other bank. This was annoying. What was worse, he suddenly put down his rod and ran. I knew what that meant. Their keeper was into a fish in the Broad Pool. I stood on the opposite bank, inwardly cursing, whilst it was landed. The ghillie was so excited that he bungled the gaff. He managed to get the fish out of the water and then fell flat on his back, with the fish between his legs. Eventually they secured it, and held it up for me to see. About 12 lbs. I shouted insincere congratulations.

The Upper Crombie and Tammy's Burn were blank again, and I thought it was time to try the upper reaches at about three o'clock. Wynne and a Colonel Helensdale (like Colonel Up and Mr. Down in the comic pictures) were splashing about in the Mill Pool. We exchanged pleasantries. They went downstream to trout, and I went right up to start at the Top Pool. The rain had stopped at about two

o'clock, though the wind was still strong in the east. In the
Top Pool a trout of 15 ozs. went for my Bulldog and was
duly slain. Poor condition, and still something wrong
with the vent. All the Craigenkillie trout have, this year. In
the Upper Ardgalley I lost my last Bulldog by catching it
on an uncharted invisible stone in midstream: also all the
gut. Here was a pretty state of things. I tried a Mar Lodge
down to the Crooked Pot and then decided that something
bright was needed. The wind had dropped and it was cold
and dull. I put on the Will's Fancy (which Macdonald had
laughed to scorn) for the stretch below the Island Pool,
where I had yesterday's fish. It was past six o'clock. Just
the right time to arrive at the Mill Pool. With the wind
dropped I found that I could cast perfectly ad infinitum.
But I was tired. Half-way down the Mill Pool, at the tail of
the ripple, he was on. Got you, you beggar. Still the
sprung rod. It bends in a perfect arc till it gets to the break
and then kinks alarmingly. He was a powerful fish and
fought well, taking me up to the rocks at the top, to make
the party go. He had a tendency to leap. I gaffed him out
below the point, first shot, in under nine minutes. He
weighed ten pounds and I packed up for the night. This
means that Craigenkillie has killed more fish before May
than previously recorded in the Game Book: I have taken
to my rod as many fish as have been taken by previous
pre-May rods put together: and one more fish will
establish a one-rod record against the whole boiling of
them, keepers included. This is partly, but I should like to
think not entirely, because it is a good year. Edinmore has
three fish, Blairglassie two, and the people above us one.
Three cheers for Wills' Fancy.

I mustn't let this record spoil my fishing. On Monday,
the last day of April (Aprile, as Macdonald calls it), I won't
fish for salmon except before noon and after six. At least
one is not Amy Johnson.

The aged laird of Craigenkillie, upon being asked in
1896 to what he attributed his long and happy life, replied:

'Young man, I have always obsairved two rules. (*a*) I have never resisted temptation, (*b*) I have always sharpened me hooks with a carborundum.'

29. iv. xxxiv.

Sunday. I had a long lie and a bath; went up to Craigen-killie at 1.30 for the camera and talked to Macdonald; copied the map of the river and took several photographs. A dull day for photographers, but I must chance it. Then I went and fetched Tommy Watts, the genius who first began to make the Bentley go. We footled about till 7.30. Mrs. Watts made me go in to tea. We saw a heron fishing, and three teal. Paid debts over car. Still not running on one switch. Boring day. But Tommy Watts is a grand person.

The water is going *down*, and I shall use a small Kessler's Fancy to-morrow.

Macdonald took me over the castle. It will do. I must get a book on toxicology.

On a blank day one can think about fishing. My mind keeps going back to the people who talk about patience. Put it like this. A man who is fishing for salmon has a whippy piece of wood, attached to the end of which there is a bit of string perhaps as long as a cricket pitch. He has got to wave his piece of wood in such a way as to extend the string behind him and then drop it in front of him in an absolutely straight line. Many people have difficulty in managing a crop, whose lash is only about four feet long. He repeats this delicate feat perhaps seven hundred times in a day, speculating every time about the exact place where he wants the string to land, and he is content to do this for three days running without killing a fish, provided that he kills one on the fourth. This looks to me like a good tribute to the excitement of the kill.

People seem to think that a fisherman sits in the shade of a pollard willow watching his float, whilst the countryside dreams about him, the cuckoo sings, and the cattle draw the grass. It has snowed or sleeted almost every day that I have been here. I have walked perhaps ten miles a day, and been at it nearly twelve hours a day—in the sleet. This is not because I am tough or obstinate, but because the joys are so *thrilling* (a queer word to use about an art that has nothing to do with steeplechases or motor-racing) that it would be unthinkable to do anything else. The fisherman fishes as the urchin eats a cream bun, from lust. You might as well talk about the patience of Tarquin.

30. iv. xxxiv.

Icabod.

Second thoughts on 30. iv. xxxiv.

More and more things transpire about the habits of fish, or at least according to Macdonald's wisdom. They will not take on a day which is expecting rain.

To-day was broiling hot. The first thing I heard at 9.30 was the plop of a salmon jumping in the Mill Pool, and the last thing I heard at eight o'clock was the same. Between those hours I tried every lure in the box, on casts from 3x to light salmon. The water was very clear and down. I never touched a fish, though I *saw* more than enough of them. One particular 14-pounder in the Mill Pool used my line as a skipping rope most of the day. I had a last desperate attempt to fascinate him at 7.30, giving him everything from a ¼-inch Claret and Teal to a Gordon of about three inches. But no, he was merely suffering from *joie de vivre*. To-night the rain is to come, and to-morrow he will be running. Not so courtly as the Spaniards, I called him low words to his face.

So my rod has only equalled the standing pre-May record (1926) established by three gentlemen: but Macdonald and I have made a new high-water mark between us. The Game Books go back to about 1890. Such an amount of luck is enough to be thrilled about. At least I had the decency to stop fishing at eight o'clock, instead of sitting up all night with a worm. To-morrow, my last happy, chaste, sober and early-rising day (how Cobbett would have patted me on the head), I shall devote to trout.

To-day the only thing I caught was a trout of 2 ozs. I smacked its bottom and put it angrily back.

What is the small black bird with a white breast? Dipper, diver or water ousel?

The salmon that leaped was not *running*. He stayed in the same place and leaped to express himself.

1. v. xxxiv.

A happy day, for I forgot it was my last until we were back in the gun-room. The rain missed us, though it poured in Grantly. The salmon were still leaping as with yesterday, the strongish wind was in the west, and the sky was cloudy though bright. We went after trout, taking the water bailiff, in order to send some away for examination. The vent is hard, protrusive and sometimes bleeding (generally inflamed like a boil), and the belly goes blackish quickly after killing. They are in poor condition. Macdonald had five, I had four and the water bailiff two. They were taking very small flies, olive duns and march browns, but it was not a taking day. I scrambled about in the river in waders and enjoyed myself and sat about and smoked. We ought to have had more fish, except for the smallness of the fly. I lost a dozen or so, two or three quite powerful pulls. People who say that very small flies kill as well as big ones are cranks. It stands to reason. Macdonald lost five fish in one passage over the Mill Pool. But of course you sometimes have to have them.

The cow was out as usual. It is not a laughable spectacle really. There is something horrible about it. The horse is poor, but *not* a scarecrow. Somehow this makes it worse. And the man has a toiling face.

Back in the gun-room it was terrible. I had to gather all my traps together, and then I couldn't bear to go. So we sat and smoked and all the time I could see that Macdonald was wanting his tea, but I couldn't say good-bye. It is horrible to be sure that it will be for good. I said I would be back with the witch in September, but I doubt it. The Rothmore is so beautiful between its lovely barren hills, and unattainable. It is odd to think that it will be here whilst I am there, and Macdonald will be in the gun-room, and the stones in the river (except two), and the clouds on the top of Groamach.

3. v. xxxiv.

I can't pretend that I was pleased to leave heaven for the Shire, nor that it was a happy surprise when, after averaging exactly 50 from Glasgow to Carlisle, the car broke down again at Penrith. It sheared the drive between the two magnetos. It was thus by dint of tedious trains and broken-down taxis that I returned to the bosom of my own county, and felt it grow about me indifferently. It made no profuse welcomes. Only, when I slipped into Shireham, the curfew bell was still ringing: as it rings, even in this hurried year of grace, every evening at eight o'clock.

4. v. xxxiv.

Nothing ever happens in the Shire, but in a queer way we have our own curiosities. Our patron saint, for instance, was St. Rumbold, who only lived for three days. In the south part of the county there was once a man who won a battle on a bull. At Water Lovell lived the Reverend John Mason, who believed himself a new Elias and announced the second coming. His followers called the village Mount Sion. On the occasion of the end of the world they dwelt in tents, stood on top of a rise to watch the surrounding countryside destroyed, sang, danced, jumped and frantically clapped their hands to the sound of violin, pipe and tabor. The world continued, and some time afterwards Mr. Mason left it. He prefaced this event by prophesying his resurrection after three days. The succeeding vicar was forced to open his coffin, in order to prove that he was still there; yet the village continued to affirm that he had risen, and that many had spoken to him after death. This, I think, is a nice example of firm rural face-saving.

5. v. xxxiv.

It was a wrench to come back, in one's conscious mind, but perhaps subconsciously a kind of ease. One gives in to coming home, and it is right to know where one lives. That is the trouble with the theoretician: he knows how he thinks, but not where he is. It is salutary to have many contacts with the world about one: not only with people, but also with the trees which bower the place where one has left one's car, with the interests and occupations of the place itself, with its history. I am an individual, living my curious life according to certain lights: but so also is every place I set my foot in, a thing infinitely older and more packed with history than myself, a thing from which one can draw interest and information. The town-dweller fuddles through Fleet Street without the faintest idea of its individuality. Not so the countryman. Old Pat, uneducated though he may be, is interested, expanded, completed by his knowledge that a gibbet stood at this corner, where perhaps Lord Beaverbrook does not even know what people passed through Ludgate. It is a kind of humanity, a contact with one's fellow men, even if dead. If they are men who lived ten hundred years ago, they are those who have left their impression on England. They turn one's eyes outward.

I drive through the Shire at a good speed, but it is

seldom a question only of speed. There are the crops to think about, and how they are doing, but also there are the old people who made the place what it is. It is not a reactionary interest. I seldom think back purely for the pleasure of reminiscence. I think of the Mad Hatter of Shireham, who lived first on bran, water and turnip tops (at a cost of ¾d. a week) and finally on a simple diet of dock leaves and grass, not because he is an interesting antiquity, but because he had his own effect on the place I am in. The place develops, plunges into the future, because of him and me. He had a sackcloth suit, built his own hut, preached, meditated, saw 'visions of the Paradise of God' while digging his parsnips, was an astrologer, a doctor with 120 patients, and a witch. He was imprisoned at Clerkenwell, without any food at all, until a dog, on a kind thought, brought him a bit of bread. He was a haber-dasher of hats at Butterbury, but he would pray behind the counter. He sold everything to give to the poor, after he had been a soldier, a vegetarian, a Quaker, a hermit, an author, a haberdasher, a doctor, and a wise man. Eventu-ally they called him The Mad Hatter; and he gave birth to a hero of Alice in Wonderland.

6. v. xxxiv.

Second thoughts on Craigenkillie.

The fact was that there had been a lot of water in March, quite an unusual amount, and this brought the fish. The spate which followed in the middle of April finished the good work and there was a much larger number of salmon than there usually is as high as this before May. In fact, we probably ought to have killed more fish.

Perhaps this is pessimistic. We got the fish we deserved. And at any rate I was terribly happy.

I must kill a tunny, get a gun in a syndicate on a grouse moor, fetch a salmon of 40 lbs. from Norway, be des-

perately busy in all directions in order to make up for
Craigenkillie.

Macdonald was a very lovely person. It was even
torture to leave the post office, where they had been so
kind and made such a sweet offer of their coconuts.

I shall remember a lot of things about Macdonald: how
he always said that the water was in good or bad 'orrder':
how collectedly he moved his tough body, which in a
townsman would have lumbered, over boulders that kept
me lagging behind, and up slopes of one in one, carrying
rods and game bag with two or three heavy fish in it: how
he did not suffer from the bugbear of 'getting his feet wet,'
but walked in the water as cheerfully as on the land,
knowing that an active man cannot catch cold: how philo-
sophically he replied, when I asked him whether the local
labourers didn't hate him for stopping their poaching,
'Well, I'm no weel likit.' He was the loyalest, neatest,
gentlest person. He was impossible to tire, always good-
humoured, and loved his work: the kind of man who is
neither weak nor hard. When he was at leisure he enjoyed
his shirt sleeves, like a soldier out of uniform: on Sundays
he went religiously to chapel: he was a fine man for his
food.

God bless him and his place anyhow; and good-bye to
Scotland, the loveliest country in the world.

7. v. xxxiv.

Among other lessons which I have learnt in Scotland,
there is the fact that only one hat at present manufactured
by the human race is of any use at all. A top hat may be
useful to fall into, hunting, and an unstrengthened one
may be pleasantly light for town wear; but there is only
one general purposes hat for the country, and this is the
deer-stalker or twa-snooted bonnet. If you fish in a
blizzard for a fortnight, you learn that the back of your
neck is more important that your forehead. If you fish in a

cap you find that, after a certain pitch of misery has been passed, the cap gets turned back to front. It is better to have a wet face than a wet back. The twa-snooted bonnet protects both quarters, besides having two admirable flaps with which it is possible to comfort the ears in a snowstorm. I shall have to order one of these, to make up for it in the Shire.

Whan that the month of May
Is comen, and that I here the foules singe,
And that the floures ginnen for to springe,
Farwel my book and my devocioun.

CHAUCER

I helped Tom Bourne to deliver one of his mares of a foal to-day. It was a grisly business in a way, as you have to actually haul the creature out with a rope; but it makes up for itself. For one thing, you are helping: you did not yourself invent the system of birth, and are making it better for the mare, not worse. Also there is a sense of creation about it. There were more horses in the field when I left it than there were when I went in. It is the kind of visible increase that pleased Cobbett.

It was exciting. She had been due to foal for nearly twenty-four hours. When we went out after tea Mark was there watching, and he beckoned to us. We went with the rope and an iron bar, in case leverage was needed in emergency, and stood under a hedge at the top of the field, two hundred yards away. She was down, and they said that she wouldn't be long now. We stood and watched, talking involuntarily in low voices. She got up again, looking rocky, but nothing happened. The other mare, Poppet, had foaled two weeks ago. Poppet's foal suddenly came trotting across from her mother and began to suck milk from Blossom, who allowed it without protest. The foal trotted back. We thought it might make him scour. Tom had never seen anything like this happen before. After about twenty minutes Blossom went down again, and rolled on her back. She held her legs unnaturally, as if she were dead or in pain. We began to stir uneasily. It was obviously beginning to happen. She got up again clumsily, and tried to crop some grass, and turned her back to us, and we could see that there was something white coming out. We walked quietly downhill towards her, till she lay down for the third time, and cut the bag, and looped the rope round the soft mushroom-coloured hoofs.

We fell over when he came out, a big foal. He lay there and shivered, all legs and hoofs, but with his head up in a new country, whilst Blossom shuddered. He had come, with his lizard face and unfocused eyes, from another world. He was going to be a black horse, gelded at eighteen months, perhaps a fine specimen. We didn't know. He had the world before him.

The feature of the whole thing was lack of hurry. We let them alone for a minute or two, whilst Tom told me that a foal is born with a kind of false tongue in his mouth. I think he called it 'with a crown in his mouth.' A filly is not. We found the thing, like a bit of liver, and turned it over with our toes. Mark was reticent and offhanded about the so-called magic properties that it possessed.* Tom suggested letting Blossom see the foal, which was lying behind her, but just then she lifted her neck and looked round. The foal tried to get up, but couldn't because it didn't know what its legs were for. It had to find out about gravity. Blossom stood up and thought. They had both stopped bleeding. After a bit Tom said we should teach the foal to stand. It seems that if you can teach it to stand and suckle more quickly than it would naturally learn to do so, then its chances of survival are greater. We uncrossed its legs and held it up on them, but when we let it go it would sway, trip up, and subside. However, after we had held it up twice, it knew what it ought to aim at. It began trying to get up by itself. We went round the hedges for half an hour with the gun. When we came back it was standing laboriously on all four hocky pins, and Blossom was snuffling gently at it through her nose.

*But when I went to see the foal next day and looked for it, the thing was gone.

11. *v. xxxiv.*

The late spring is the time for finding out about birds, and I have been spending many days standing mournfully under trees, identifying young female blackbirds as chaffinches by their note. One of the sad things about birds is that none of the text-books can really be of any use. For a bird is not normally identified by its plumage. A book of bird pictures is all very well if you have the creature dead in your hand, but a real bird is not a static collection of colours: it is a thing that sings and flies. It is by flight and song that the proper identification is made, and neither of these things can satisfactorily be written down in a book. For one thing, as far as the song goes, most birds have several variations: and for another, although I have captured musical experts and taken them round with me, it seems impossible to write down a bird's music in any known or unknown notation. I had high hopes of inventing an easy means of record, of a graphlike or seismographic nature, in which, for instance, you would record the cuckoo thus: ⋀ and the skylark as follows: ⋁⋁⋁⋁⋁⋁⋁⋁⋀⋁. But it fell down on the tits, because it was incapable or representing the difference between Te—te—te—te, and Pe—Pe—Pe—Pe. In fact, there is something consonantal about birds' song (which is the reason why bird books try desperately to record their knowledge in terms of the alphabet, e.g. 'a constant repetition of two notes,* sounding like "ee-ker, ee-ker." Call, "zee, zee" and "pink, pink."') and also why country people have little phrases which birds are supposed to say. The pigeon says traditionally, 'Take two cows, Taffy,' or 'Joe's toe bleeds, Betty' if it is going to rain. But unfortunately the alphabetical approach only carries us half-way, like graphic notation, and what it really comes down to is that

*And I wonder whether anybody can identify the bird, without further help, from this description?

bird song can't be put in books. I said 'unfortunately' without thinking, because as a matter of fact it is a good thing. It means this, that ornithology, in spite of having such a long name, is bound to remain a traditional, oral and emphirical craft. You can't have a correspondence course in birds. You have to go out to them in person, with a companion to start you by experience and word of mouth, and then you have got to find out for yourself. In fact, birds are handed down apostolically. They are the kind of thing that cannot be industrialised or mechanised or mass-produced or turned into print, or efficiently pigeon-holed in the Drage Way, or Pelmanised in the abstract or put in a Blue book, or demeaned by any other modern jerry-built systems. They have got to be encountered personally, in parties preferably of not more than two, and their lore has got to be handed down in the honest old verbal chain: so that what I know comes down to me along a linked descent of gamekeepers and sons of farmers and birds-nesting little boys, each one inheriting in affectionate personal contact, generation after generation, as the honest *trade* of sculpture was handed down in Greece. Indeed, I can dream that the mentor of my mentor was possibly acquainted with this or that fact by W. H. Hudson in person, or even by Richard Jefferies. It is like being ordained.

The other incommunicable thing about birds is their flight, and this is the best way of all to distinguish them. It is all very well to know that a carrion crow is bigger than a rook and has a feathered beak. In order to make these identifications you have got to have the crow to hand, and preferably a dead rook as well for purposes of comparison. Now the carrion crow lives, I believe I am right in saying, as long as a man, is extremely destructive of game, and is hunted for that reason with much enthusiasm by gamekeepers, as well as by emotional people who object to the creature for pecking out the eyes of dying animals. It can be easily understood that a crow who may be as old as myself, and has been hunted, as he hunts, all his life, is not an easy bird to bring to hand. I want to kill him, because he eats my partridges, and so I want to be able to distinguish him. I don't want to spend hours stalking every black bird I see, in case he is a crow, and yet I want the carrion. It is not much use my knowing that he has a hairy beak, because if he has one he will be up and away before I am within two hundred yards. Book knowledge is useless. He is only about two inches longer than a rook, and at that distance the difference is not perceptible. It is true that I can learn from a book that he usually goes about singly or in pairs, whilst a rook keeps in a flock; but this rule is by no means invariable. A rook is not gregarious all the time, or perhaps his friends (for they are exclusive in their tribal system) are hidden by a fold of the field. To cut a long story short, I have got to recognise him, the most cunning of the birds, by the way he flies in the air. And he does fly differently. The rook wags his wings: the crow hoists and thrusts them. A rook leaps out of a tree: a crow falls out of it. It is as if the crow had a more toilsome body.

12. v. xxxiv.

The flight of all birds is individual. You can illustrate it best by taking the more exaggerated ones, but even a blackbird flies differently from a thrush. The hawk hovers and so does the lark;* but when the hawk stoops he drops the whole way vertically. The lark flattens out after ten feet, goes some yards horizontally, and drops again. He goes down, therefore, in a series of L's; and the last L has its base almost on the ground. You think you have marked him down at the point A, but when you go there he is really at B, perhaps ten yards farther on. It is the same

---

*But of course not in the same way. It is the difference between violently agitating the wings to keep station, and sailing by leaning against the air: a habit which has earned for the rusty-backed kestrel (who looks so much better when seen from above, perhaps from the window of a train on an embankment) his lovely title, The Windhover.

sort of thing that happens with partridges later in the season, when you mark them closer than they actually dropped, and with snipe. I have been prepared to bet my daughter's hand in marriage that a snipe was in a certain reedy clump, only to find his little ghost skewing 'chippering' away, twenty yards to the right. The Tree Pipit, another of the semi-hovering birds, comes down almost exactly like an auto-giro. He sails down to his tree-top, with wings spread out like a cupid in a holy picture, all the time shaking his tiny buff body with his song: Terwee terwee terwee terwee tweet tweet tweet tweet.

His flaggy wings, when forth he did display,
Were like two sayles, in which the hollow wynd
Is gathered full, and worketh speedy way:
And eke the pennes, that did his pineons bynd,
Were like mayne-yardes with flying canvas lynd;
With which whenas him list the ayre to beat,
And there by force unwonted passage fynd,
The clouds before him fledd for terror great,
And all the heavens stood still amazed with his threat.

THE FAERIE QUEENE

14. v. xxxiv.

The beginnings of this saga now seem irretrievably remote
and unreal. There was a kind of despair at leaving Scotland, rage with the car, and I suppose a feeling of lone-
liness. The cat's life can't be kept up indefinitely. Every
two or three years the spring must win, and then it is
bitter.

On the 4th I made Ker take me to Jimmy's, with the
intention of seeking solace in the good liquor of the Shire.
The local news was that there was somebody or other's
aerial circus in a field near. This was just the thing, and Ker
consented to come on an hour's flight. We flew proudly
and boringly over Shireham, Park, Fernley, White Horse,
and Warden, waving incessantly. There was an enormous
trailing pennant on each wing, which we thought was an
advertisement for the circus. When we got home, we
found it had been advertising Bile Beans.

The bright spot about the flight was the fact that the
landing wire on the near side struts seemed to be on the
verge of disintegration. Not knowing whether they
served some vital ballistic purpose did relieve the tedium
of the journey. It was an incredibly ancient Avro, held
together with bits of insulating tape.

I was fortunate to begin like this, because by boring me
it cured my nerves to a large extent.

When we came down I went for an aerobatic flight in a
red and newer Avro: a wildly satisfactory succession of
loops, stalling turns, zooms and contour chasing. Ker
would not come.

Smug satisfaction: Thank God I am not a gentleman. Peter, who has a good-form father, reproaches me with 'fishing-jealous,' when I ached for Macdonald's fish in Lang's Pot. Of course. Now I shall fly jealous. Why not?

It was a bright moment in a week of suppressed despair. I went to arrange about training at Credon aerodrome, and heard of a newspaper advertisement scheme. They grant you £20 towards your expenses if you are marked by the instructor as the best pupil at his aerodrome.

Then there were many days of trying to find the right coupon to fill in. On Sunday I couldn't wait any more, had sent off the entry forms, rung up the paper for permission to take my lesson before getting their official answer, and fixed a lesson for 2.30.

There was a little difficulty in swallowing my lunch.

Humphrey took us over in the Lancia. He flew during the war. He said: 'Movements almost imperceptible, and you won't feel in contact with your aeroplane at all during the first hour.' It was a piece of luck that he said this, because I had been reading a flying book and had got it into my head that one pushed things about by numbers. What he said put me in exactly the right frame of mind.

I signed a cheque in the control-room with rather a wiggly signature.

When Johnny Burn and the aeroplane turned up I stopped being nervous.

He said: 'I am only allowed to take you up to a thousand and let you fly her straight. I have to report on that.'

I was given helmet, goggles; I got in and plugged in and put on the safety belt. We started. The ground went fast, receded. The wind blew down one's back. The horizon was quite hazy to the left; on the right you could just guess it. The trees and fields and the white hangars. Middlehampton like a strawberry rash, reddish and sprawling. Scab? Wen.

Johnny Burn said: 'Now I will start the patter. The

rudder bars . . . the yawing plane . . . sit sloppily . . . etc.
Now I want you to take the rudder. Are you ready? Right.
The rudder is yours.'

I put the balls of my feet on it like a cat.

'I want you to take a mark and fly straight for it.'

I was flying straight. I had the rudder. Humphrey had
said I would not feel the controls in contact at all. I just
padded with my right foot, a millimetre almost toe-
movement or feeling of the muscles, cautiously experimental and delicate. The nose came round an inch. I did
the other foot. It worked. I was in contact. The engine was
very loud.

Then I flew straight. It was easy, but one felt a little
stupefied: Étourdi.

Johnny Burn said: 'Good. Now the joystick is more
difficult . . . the nose . . . the tail . . . the looping plane.
Now I am going to give you the joystick. Are you ready?
Right. Now you've got her altogether.'

This definitely one wouldn't be able to feel. I touched it
with finger and thumb, with a sort of capillary attraction.
There was almost a layer of air between my fingers and the
stick. We were flying straight. I had got her altogether. We
didn't fall out of the air.

I soothed, suggested, fancied, ever so little, over to the
left. The wing went down a foot. But it was perfect! We
hinted forward, the nose dropped a few inches below the
haze. Back, and it came up.

We flew straight.

Johnny Burn said: 'Now I shall turn her round. Let me
have the controls.'

We turned round.

We flew straight.

I looked at the wings now, as well as the nose, and felt
them instinctively. It was pie, and very amusing. We were
over the aerodrome. Johnny Burn kept on talking.

He said: 'If you keep your nose up and loose speed you
stall. Let me have the controls. It is like this.'

We went up and failed, went soggy. You could feel the air not pressing on the wings.

He said: 'Then you stall. Your controls won't work. There is not enough pressure on them.'

He waggled everything violently. The ailerons flapped madly, but nothing happened. The nose came down and went towards the earth. It was faintly unpleasant. Then, in the dive, the controls took over again.

Later he switched off the engine and made me take up the right gliding angle. It felt less safe when the engine was off.

He took over.

The S-turns with the engine off felt fragile. The ground was nearer, and there were people on the road, looking up. We swept in over the hedge and the ground was close. We flew along it. You would have hardly noticed when we were on.

I said, getting out: 'How many entrants are there for your newspaper scheme?'

He said: 'There are ninety. You are number 28, easily the best so far.'

This pleased me, because I didn't suspect him then of being a flatterer.

I said: 'I could have turned it round myself, I swear, and I want to go up again.'

Humphrey wanted to go home. Johnny Burn was booked till 6.30. I made Ker promise to take me back after tea, by saying I would pay for a lesson for him.

On the way home I sang '*Ai nostri monti*' and the scherzo of Brahms Quintet of F Minor, neither of them at all in tune. I also bounced on the back seat and talked volubly, until Humphrey looked cross.

We went back after tea.

We went up at once.

Johnny did the patter.

We did banking turns.

It was a different machine, I was in the back seat with the

instruments instead of the front one, and the telephone didn't properly work. I missed most of what he said. But it didn't matter a scrap. Flying is the easiest and the most amusing thing in the world. You don't fly by rules or numbers, but by instinct and by feeling the pressure of the wind on your wings. I didn't have to think about anything except my rudder bar, which is the only slightly unnatural movement. I was allowed to play with the engine, climb, glide, dive and bank. Also with the tail trimming gear. I have had 50 minutes in all. Aviators live by hours, not by days.

It was bumpy everywhere, and especially near the ground. When she bumped I thought at first it was Johnny Burn trying to make things more difficult, to see how I reacted. So I reacted firmly and this was quite good for the bumps.*

Seeing one's nose *boring* round the horizon in a steep bank is fascinating. Somehow or other one seems to be holding the roaring screw into the world's mouth, like a gigantic dentist or a road-mender with one of those drills. And all the time it turns majestically about one, and the low wing points steadily down.

From the back seat I found it more difficult to fly level.

Ker went up afterwards and did well. This made me envious. We have made side bets on who (*a*) loops first, (*b*) lands first, (*c*) gets his certificate first. Catch as catch can.

The chairman of the club talked to me meanwhile; he seemed to like it.

Then we went to the bar with Johnny Burn till he went home. He must be a flatterer, a rogue. Naturally he is an angel and flies like one and smiles at everybody all the time. I wouldn't trust him with a farthing, a drink, or my fiancée; but he could have my heart. It is like this with all good and great people. The master of an art can afford to over-ride the common standards, indeed is forced to do so. He is doing something perfectly, and this kind of

*? (Later).

creation costs him such a lot that he cannot afford the time
for other things. Johnny is such a magnificent aviator, and
such a perfect person, that he can get away with anything.
He can let you drive twenty-four-miles for a lesson and
then call it off. He could, if he wanted to, strangle his
whole family, burn down the house, and murder innocent
children in their beds; but he would still be irreproachable.
I don't know why. He had flown five or six or more
thousand hours: heaven knows how many. I offered him a
cheque for £40, to cover insurance in case of accidents, if he
would let me fly solo at once. He didn't even laugh at me.
He said he could teach me in four hours; but this was
blarney. Also I am terribly afraid that the early easiness
may be succeeded by a stage at which I shall get stuck and
dejected.

When they turned us out of the bar we went by mistake
to an obscene road-house pub that catered for the urban
scourings of Middlehampton. It was off the road, and
nothing to show that it was there. But after you had driven
a few hundred yards down a side lane you found a positive
Derby-day of motor-cars, and a big pub with lots of
rooms all full of drunks and women from the miniature.
Wen. I didn't like them very much. But we had sandwiches and more beer. All this is dim. We left a note for
Humphrey when we got home, challenging him to a
trans-Atlantic flight.

This morning, when I got up at seven, there was an
electric light bulb in my pocket.

15. v. xxxiv.

The stoutest period of English history, the first half of
the nineteenth century, still lives vaguely in the country.
The two parties which governed England before modern
politics began were called the Blues and the Reds.
Nowadays Reds just mean Russians, but in the Shire we

use the word in the old sense. I have the fortune to live in a
village which was once Red, and to be subject to a little
poaching from what was once the Reddest village of them
all. My village is no longer of the old colour, because it has
been laid waste by a swarm of boy scouts and musical
societies and tea fights, which have effectively brought it
to the fundlord's heel. But Silston keeps to the tradition. It
was a woodland community once, for the King's great
deer forest covered thirty-two square miles. Silston never
had a squire and always had the rights to grazing and
firewood which Cobbett approved of in Sussex. I dare say
Silston men insisted on leather leggings and plum pud-
ding, too. Anyway, the forest was their poaching ground
(penalty a year's imprisonment: or death if the deer was
taken in a private park), and they called no man master.
Their old church had no resident rector, and was dedicated
to the devil in the course of a morris dance on the roof, on
the same day that it was dedicated to God. A fine, friendly,
lawless population, they stood no nonsense from the
penalising magistracy. The woods had dwindled and been
enclosed; they had been stolen away from the poor to give
to the rich; but Silston countrymen maintained the right to
their old perquisites. I can't help stealing a story about
Silston. There was once a savage parson-magistrate who
incurred the wrath of the Forest. A band of men marched
to his woods to go nutting, encountered his keepers, beat
them in a stand-up battle, and accomplished their purpose.
The next night the guards were doubled, but so was the
attacking force. The result was the same. On the third
night a contingent of no less than 160 persons marched to
war, and was again victorious. The magistrate collected
every able-bodied man whom he could coerce with
money or influence, and invaded Silston to arrest the
ringleaders. The village was ready with a cartload of hedge
stakes. When the attacking column appeared it used the
church bells to summon its own forces. The inhabitants of
every age and sex armed themselves with the stakes and

beat the magistrate back to his kennel. The Bow Street Runners were now called in, to be met with scythes and the impossibility of making single arrests. They would have had to arrest them all or none. It seems that the Runners were sensible people, for they achieved a compromise by pacific action, backed with beer. The Silston men gave themselves up, on the understanding that the matter should not be pressed, and they escaped with nominal fines: so that everybody except the magistrate was happy.

This same parson was the man who had a fall in a deep dyke when hunting with the Duke's, and, upon asking a Silston man for a hand out, received the somewhat okkerd reply: 'You wunt be wanted afoore next Sunday.' Okkerd (awkward) is the Shire word which means anything between surly and nuisance-making.

It was this nosey parson, also, who ended up the victim of the best practical joke I know. He fancied himself on his humanity towards animals, as so many people do who are inhuman to their fellow men, and he particularly disapproved of carters who sat on the shafts of their loaded wagons. One day he was riding to Shireham when he overtook a boy who was practising this very offence. He gave him a pompous lecture, which the boy received in silence, and rode on his way. Immediately his back was turned, there came an outburst of loud and obscene profanity about magistrates and parsons and squires and all their works. The Squire turned back in a rage, rated the boy, and turned his horse in the worst of tempers. But the moment he began to ride away an even more exhaustive commentary was launched behind him. He rode to Shireham, had a warrant made out, and caused the boy to be brought before the bench. When he had delivered an harangue to his brother magistrates about the enormity of the boy's conduct and the signal punishments which should be meted out for such an insult towards the justiciary, the boy's father (who had been hiding inside the wagon) went into the dock and conclusively proved that the boy had been dumb since birth.

16. v. xxxiv.

Johnny Burn is a grand person. He is at the same time quite undependable, except in the air. I cadged a lift over to-day from the Beam, 24 miles at least, and booked a lesson for 3.30 by telephone. When we got there Johnny claimed that it was too gusty for flying. After waiting about till 6.30 I came home in black despair.

(*a*) Because I can't wait till the newspaper competition is over, I have joined the club and paid up. Johnny swears that this will make no difference to his report that I am his best pupil (if I still am after the other 68), but I can't trust him. He says it with the bland candour of a very naughty little boy; and it will obviously pay him to recommend another entrant, since I am already hooked. So this outlook is blank.

(*b*) I have enthusiastically, but only pro. tem., given up smoking cigarettes, drinking, and everything else. This is enough to make any one wild.

(*c*) I had to go to a pub with the Beam, to make up for his coming to the aerodrome with me, and a pub is not much fun on Grapefruit Squash.

Altogether it has been a hellish day.

Booked two lessons for Saturday.

My first lesson was G-ABJT, the second G-AHET. I much prefer the former.

17. v. xxxiv.

It is not only a question of sorrow at leaving Scotland. It is partly a question of fear. I have always been afraid of things: of looking a fool, of being hurt, of death. Death particularly, and probably more than with most people. Does everybody claim to be unusually sensitive, just as everybody claims to have more to suffer than the next man, and to possess a sense of humour? At any rate I do. The fear of death has always been something living, an idea of being shut conscious in a black box with worms and earth, or, as that passed, of what the dead people miss. It is the penalty paid for sensibility. If one likes the shape of clouds and people, or the sun on one's knees; if one is aware of pleasures, can see and feel; if one is avaricious, ravening for more life: death is a sense of loss. One has to avert one's mind from it. Intrinsically I cannot feel now that even at a hundred I should be ready to let go. As an undergraduate it was the fear of letting go, the fear of a precipitous drop to an unknown destination. Now it is not mystical: only physical fear of pain, and desire for more life.

I have always been a coward: afraid of things that hurt, body or soul. At school I was horribly afraid of being beaten. Before I fractured my leg I was terrified at the idea of a broken bone, imaginatively terrified. And now I am afraid, not of the idea, but of the pain. I am afraid of people, of personal contacts. Some of my friends, who suffer from the same fear, have had the natural sense to give in to it and become happily shy. Unfortunately I didn't do this. I had to go out to meet the personal contacts in armour: a shell like the protection of the hermit crab. One can understand a lobster wanting to pinch a hermit crab behind.

And now it is flying. I am afraid of aeroplanes. They stay in the air for purely scientific reasons, which means for me by faith alone. I am frightened for the wings and struts and wires; and of the sensation, which really must be a remarkable one, of an aviator whose collection of fabrics fails him at ten thousand feet. I understand that the maximum velocity attained by the falling human body is 120 m.p.h. That means that one would have leisure for speculation during nearly a minute and a half.

So, as with the personal contacts, one is forced to battle.

Perhaps it is true that the best method of defence is attack. Because I am afraid of things, of being hurt and death, I have to attempt them. This journal is about fear.

18. v. xxxiv.

But it is worth while to live with a little bit of danger. One is so surrounded in peace time with the depravity of the modern world. If for my whole life I were to redeliver the same lectures, nag at the same people, prattle the same scandal, what else would there be for it except to take earnestly to drink? One would forget the foulness of the world and give oneself an illusion of happiness at any rate. Even sitting in the same chair rots one's soul. Decent men ought to break all their furniture every six months. Failing that, they ought to fly. The objective of an uncomfortable or perilous life is the enjoyment of comfort and safety in between.

19. v. xxxiv.

It was just as windy to-day, from the S.W., but Johnny was sick of waiting, for he took us up. Peter came too, and I let him fly first. It was his first time in the air at all, but he took to it like a Mayfly. The wind was horribly gusty, I thought, but it must have been my bad flying.

When we started Johnny said: 'It is no good for taking off or landing to-day. We'll just have general flying practice. You may take off with me.' He explained how to take off and we started. It was ET, who is in my opinion heavy and lumpish. When we were about twenty feet up, he said: 'Now you've got her.' I took over and swung round the aerodrome, gathering height. She seemed to buck about in a horrible way, and I felt ham-handed and stupid. Anyway I have got a cold—caught. It is my affliction to catch from other people what I don't deserve myself.

We did figures of eight. I was a fool. The nose was coming up or going down, and the angle of bank constantly altering. The machine never flew round the stick at all. It was a constant succession of bucking lurches. Johnny was faintly cross. He said my hands were not as good as last time. I knew they weren't. It was because his movements of the stick had been so pronounced whilst we were taking off (on account of the gusts or to emphasise the movements to me?) I was pulling and hauling her about. It was degrading.

Then I got sick of the petty little banks and tried a steep one of my own. Johnny shouted: 'Don't bank so steeply! You DON'T KNOW how to do it.' So that game was squashed. I went on doing these humiliating and loutish corners. After a bit he was satisfied, and said: 'Well, that was all right'; after my nose had kept directly on the horizon for about three circuits.

Then we did glides and climbs, leaving the throttle and cheese cutter to me. As a matter of fact I flew her all the time we were up; so that at least I got on terms with the engine revs, which I had to see to, and the flying speed. Johnny had, so far as I remember, no instruments in the front cockpit.

The cheese cutter has to be back when you are gliding, as this is its non-active position. When you push it forward it puts a spring action on the stick, which tends to hold the latter forward, and thus the nose down. The machine is so constructed as to be tail heavy with the engine on (why?) and thus needs the forward tendency of the cheese cutter to fly level, unless the pilot is to be constantly pressing forward with his stick. When the engine is off, the machine glides naturally if the cheese cutter is pulled back, i.e. put out of action. That is to say: an aeroplane is so constructed as to balance in the air *without* its engine power and is *not* balanced when the power is on. The cheese cutter balances it in the latter case.

Answer to my 'why' above: You must be balanced

without your engine, because then you have nothing to
help you, but you can afford to be unbalanced with your
engine, because then the engine can be used to redress the
balance.

In gliding I must (*a*) throttle back, (*b*) pull back the
cheese cutter, meanwhile holding up the nose, (*c*) allow
her to assume her natural gliding angle gently, as soon as
the cheese cutter is off.

In switching on again I must (*a*) put on throttle, (*b*) push
forward the cheese cutter, meanwhile tending to hold
down the nose, (*c*) climb again gently as soon as the cheese
cutter is on, (*d*) throttle back to 1,800 revs and air speed of
about 60 climbing.

When I had finished these games I did gliding turns.
When banking without engine you need (*a*) practically no
rudder, (*b*) a great deal of bank, (*c*) to keep the nose up, (*d*)
and *no* hold-off-bank. The last condition confused me and
made me stupid: the more so because Johnny did not tell
me about it until I was half-way through. I landed (Johnny
did, of course, whilst I followed his movements) feeling
(*a*) not a brilliant airman, but (*b*) that I should do better
next time.

During tea the world and his wife flew round: half a
dozen machines buzzing and ticking. The Yellow Peril
proceeded to fly between the hangars, and practically in
and out of the tea-room windows, drawing from Johnny
the bitter ejaculation: 'And now just let his engine cut out!'
His voice went resonant and pontifical, dropping with
measured emphasis from note to note. 'Croydon
Aerodrome,' he said, 'if you please. Will you send the
breakdown van? And the fire engine? And the ambulance?
And the doctors? And the nurse?

'And,' said Johnny, 'the undertaker, if you please.'

It was a mournful, noble and magniloquent apostrophe:
ending on a silence that was right, minatory but not
scaremongering, horrific but not unpleasant.

We had a lovely drive home, and went out after dinner

to see if we could hear a nightingale. I can sometimes tell, by their notes, nightingale, blackbird, thrush, robin, chaffinch, tit, sparrow, tree-pipit, cuckoo, pigeon, jackdaw, rook, night-jar, oyster catcher, curlew, plover, sandpiper, magpie, wren highly doubtful, and other such common objects as mallard and owl of course. Starling, imitating, never. Probably a good few others, such as the canary; but what a miserable list!

It has been an almost perfect day, and suffers from the disease common to such days: that it was not quite perfect and eternal.

20. v. xxxiv.

Here is what I should call a common fisherman's day. The Shire has no trout rivers in it, so that occasionally one gets desperate and drives twenty miles to the nearest scummy canal, on a rumour that trout are there reported. I drove Willie to the Cher to-day, and we fished its silent expanses for four hours, in a north-east wind that finally brought rain, without killing, or raising, or even seeing a fish. Yet it was a perfectly good day, memorable in at least three directions. Almost the first bird I saw was a sandpiper, who fled downstream in great alarm and reminded me of Craigenkillie. Then Willie put up a mallard duck who was piloting a brood of twelve. The little brown-and-yellow creatures, abandoned by their mother, hung together so closely that you could have picked the whole lot up with one lift of a landing net. They crowded breast to breast, twisted round and round by the current, paddling for dear life and keeping up a continuous chorus of cheeps. The mother hung about nervously, torn between her children and the fear of man: I saw her plane down in the field behind us, a picture of furtive anxiety. Finally there was a sheep on her back in a hollow, who looked as if she had been there some time. It is a pleasure to a countryman, particularly on a strange farm, to turn these creatures over. The pleasure is manifold. For one thing I cannot understand why God should have invented an animal which can't get up if it lies on its back (it seems a notable error in natural selection), and so, in contemplating the sheep, there is an opportunity for admiring the wonders of creation. You would not have thought that a sheep had much in common with a turtle, but it has. There is also the satisfaction of doing something useful anonymously, and of touching a creature which will not usually let you get up to it, and of helping a thing which fears you; thereby, I suppose, puzzling it a good bit.

There was a fourth pleasure. I saw the first Mayfly of the season, a green drake, and walked processionally beside him, down the bank. The Mayfly doesn't generally happen till June nowadays: but we call him by his old name still. He was a genuine Mayfly before the adoption of the new calendar, and country memories are long.

21. v. xxxiv.

The northern part of the Shire was once a prodigious forest, and there are still remains of it. When I get my late-season invitations to the big shoot at Milton I am on the borders of the most impressive woodlands that remain—Sealseye Forest. We have to drive through it for a mile or two to get there. The great trees stand, safe and impassive. Trees are said to feel safe in woods, because they are together.

But Sealseye is not truly in the Shire. The great shire forest was Whistlewood, once over twenty thousand acres, now dwindled into three or four extensive coverts like Howling Wood, where the Duke's hounds are still sure to get stuck. It is a long hack home down the Welsh Lane after a day in the Friday country, but one can think of the Welsh drovers who used it as their London route. The road goes straight and never seems to end; it was once a forest route. The lawless foresters of Whistlewood and

Silston used it since Henry the Third, and before. It was as full of highwaymen and outlaws as any woodland of Robin Hood's. When the Silston men came back from fairs along their tree-full tracks they used to light fires at intervals of half a mile. These were not for the purposes of heat, but of illumination. The Silston folk came back in bands, waiting at the lighted beacons if they became separated from their companions, making a dash through the dark interstices all together: but there was always somebody robbed of his fair winnings before Silston and Whistlewood went safe to bed.

22. v. xxxiv.

I scrounged a lift off Ker, and had lunch at the club, waiting for Johnny Burn. The weather is getting sunny again and the wind more sensible. To-day it was practically from the west.

Johnny thought it hopeless for landings, but consented to a lesson. He said we should have ET, and I said I preferred JT. It turned out that JT would be ready in five minutes, so we waited for her. We talked about outside spins (I had asked to do spins if landings were impossible) and matrimonial difficulties and the Champion Boy Aviator (aet: 17) who was over to luncheon. Johnny had taught him (after 30 hours) and now he has gone to Southport. Southport gets the advertisement credit in to-day's daily paper. Johnny was anxious to knock him down, but I confess that he had a shy childish and undependable expression which charmed myself. Johnny was in a belligerent mood and sent off messages in all directions: to a lady at Carlands, that he would smack her bottom if she didn't send him the flying suits which he ordered, and that quickly; to the Boy Aviator (though this he only breathed to the empyrean) that he would kill the little beggar if he tried to say a word. He went away without trying, and this annoyed Johnny all the more.

We got away quite soon and climbed to 2,100, when Johnny asked me the height. I carefully said 2,000. At 2,700 I maintained that it was 2,500. I was not taking chances.

Johnny said: 'Very well. Now you stall her, kick on left rudder, and she spins. When you want to come out, you put on opposite rudder, ease the stick forward, and bring yourself out of the dive.' I had been reading David Garnett's account of a spin, all about a jewelled roulette board, and felt ready to be interested.

'Now,' said Johnny.

The nose was up. I watched the A.S.I. It went back— 70—60—50—45. We hung helpless and horribly precarious, infinitely far above the earth and *unattached*. The wind was not under the wings. We were just a bundle of sticks and boxes in the air.

'Now rudder,' said Johnny.

He kicked the thing viciously on, and pulled the stick right back into his stomach. The nose went over sideways, dropped in an absolutely sickening impotence, screwing as it dropped. It was hideous and suicidal. There was no aeroplane, only a silent plummet of horribly heavy lead leaping at the bosom of the earth. There was no sky. I can describe things often, but this not at all. It was the dive, the inception,* that was the terror. She seemed so to leap and lose her wings, plunge in an engineless (even the sound was gone) somersault of nothingness but overleftwards fall. I was not afraid in my imagination, but in a concrete sense, as if it were only my lower centres, those which I share with the hunted fox, that were shouting danger. I was hardly frightened at all in the human sense, indeed I remained attentive, but my ancestral self-preservation swooned away. Then the earth began to spin. There were no jewels, no roulette board, and it wasn't half so slow as I expected. Only a lot of vertiginous brown fields, going

*JT lacked Handley Page slots.

round clockwise and far too fast. We were pointing into
the middle of the earth and I was pressing to the right side
of the cockpit. The human part of my mind attended to the
controls. The fields still went round, long enough for me
to wonder whether we oughtn't to stop them. The right
rudder went on very decidedly. The stick seemed central,
if wobbly. I don't think I noticed it going forward. The
fields stopped and my head lolled correspondingly to the
left side of the cockpit. I felt as if we were beginning to spin
the other way. The engine roared. I thought one came out
gradually. Perhaps we had been beginning to come out
before the engine went on. Anyway, there was the horizon
almost instantly.

Johnny said: 'Now you've got her.'

The altimeter said 2,000.

Seven hundred feet—the length of time, I suppose, that
one would take falling off a skyscraper.

For the rest of the half-hour I did gliding turns.

I did them fairly well, as soon as I had remembered to
put on hardly any rudder and *no* hold-off bank. Johnny
said that I was doing them well.

I sometimes forget to get level before doing an ordinary
bank, and try it with my nose too high.

As soon as I was beginning to feel that four more gliding
turns would put me comfortable with them, Johnny said
we should land. I asked if I might put him in position, and
was allowed. I got him within about a hundred yards of
where I wanted to be, and he was not displeased. He said:
'That was all right, but we should have overshot.' I had
rather overshoot this aerodrome, into the hedge, than
undershoot it into the road. We went round once more,
did S-turns down to a couple of hundred feet. Johnny took
over, sideslipped off height.

It seems at present that I shall never learn to land. I have
absolutely no criterion for judging height. At one moment
one is obviously what one would call high, and at another
moment not. There seems to be no intermediate stage.

There was a road underneath, with cars and people staring up. Then there was a lot of grass very close, and we ruminated over it for a moment and sat down.

Ker was busy wrecking my camera (he had already taken off the back and exposed the whole film) when we taxied up.

He said with a horrid leer: 'Well, I didn't see any spins.'

Johnny said: 'We did one, over there.'

Walking back to the car, Ker said, with even more offensive penetration: 'Did you do it yourself?'

Naturally I said 'Yes,' and then had to make up a story.

Driving home, I suddenly realised that I was feeling sick: the kind of sickness that one has when one has taken Mothersills and can't vomit. I also realised that I did not agree at all with David Garnett, that I had been wise not to ask to do one myself, that I shall do it next time, and that I shall be landing the time after.

I *like* gliding turns.

Theoretically I rather like spins.

I think Chatterly is going to have kittens.

23. v. xxxiv.

The Swan and Castle is rather a reserved hotel, its bar catering for the higher classes: farmers, tradesmen, the auctioneer and myself. A fruitful topic of reminiscence there is the former glory of the Shire Yeomanry. In the spacious days, the heart of my shire regulated its pulses with the muscles of the great house at Park. Its master was a duke, its visitors royal, its tenants exiled kings. So of course the duke had a troop of yeomanry.

The greatest occasion that Yeomanry ever had took place one summer day, within living memory. Everybody at the Swan and Castle remembers it with reverence. During the annual fortnight's camp there was a route march to Chase, another noble residence. It was the hottest day of the year, indeed of many years, and the Yeomanry were not accustomed to forced marches. The neighbouring nobleman was intent upon showing a due appreciation of the honour paid to him, and he provided whisky *carte blanche*. Beer would have been churlish. Unfortunately he forgot to provide water; and all the wells were dry. 'We had to drink it,' explain the now ageing yeomen pathetically, 'or perish miserably of thirst.' They drank. In the afternoon there was a grand review. Troop after troop wheeled past the saluting base—in vain. Before reaching the critical point every yeoman had fallen out of the saddle; and it took a full week-end before the last of them had found his way home.

I am glad to say that the doings of these noble fellows have been suitably commemorated, by hanging their colours in the chapel of an educational institution that has been erected since the regiment was disbanded.

25. v. xxxiv.

I went up to Penrith to-day, to fetch the Bentley. It meant catching a train at noon, and being back again to work next morning, after driving all night. This is a great pleasure, if you don't have to do it too often. It was pleasant to stop at road-house coffee stalls in the black of the night, and to find in the light inside all sorts and conditions of people: people as unshaven as oneself, lorry drivers, honest men looking like villains, villains trying to look like honest men, but without exception people on strange errands. For errands must be strange which will keep their emissaries travelling, enduring, whilst everything sleeps: even if they are only market errands to Covent Garden. The night was bitterly cold, and a snatch of hot coffee and firelight, rubbing one's frozen elbows before the same sort of wayside hearths that had warmed Dick Turpin, made one feel an enduring specimen of this sleeping race. It was fine to drive the moors in the numb night, to drive fast in a motor-car made for it: the only kind of motor which I have driven far without feeling bored. It was fine to see the sun rising cold and yellow on the near side, whilst the night, long before sunrise, retreated on the off: to feel the dew and the slight mist: to think of the test pilot, high in the cirro-cumulus clouds of dawn, feeling as keen-set as oneself: to overtake another early bird in a fast motor, and to race him by common consent to Middle-hampton, all before breakfast in the quickening sun.

26. v. xxxiv.

To-day it seemed silly to spin, because the wind had dropped at last and it was perfect for landings. Johnny had been away at Hockester, watching a Credon team competing in a cross-country map-flying competition. He came back at about 4.30, with the news that JT appeared to have lost himself. Whilst he was having tea a blue moth turned up and circled the aerodrome. It had five tries at landing, but held off every time as if suffering from nerves. What tiny wind there was altered every two minutes and made the wind stockings look confusing. They mostly blew in different ways. The moth came down at last, almost over-shooting, and then rather sportingly took off again at once, to do it properly. He had two more attacks of nerves and then landed with a bump. When he had taxied up, he said: 'Well, you must admit a show like that has its amusing side.' This was true. Personally I had thought him an amateur who had never landed before, and I rather expected him to make a nice bounce, pancake, or gently turn over. I hoped he would. Most of the club turned out to watch him. Later on he said that he had found his watch loose in the back cockpit, jammed behind the stick wires.

Johnny said: 'We will do landings.'

After we had taxied up to the start, he said forgetfully: 'Have I let you take off with me yet?'

I said: 'No.'

He explained. You must open up the throttle gently to full, holding down her nose. The stick eases off to central. Then you find she is off the ground and ever so gently let her climb. But the important thing is to keep her straight. As the wind veers she tends to yaw, and this must be instantly, firmly corrected.

He said: 'Right. I will leave her to you, but I'll be there to take over if necessary.'

I opened the throttle, and we were off. The stick was quite hard. I busily aimed at a straight course, and corrected even when there wasn't any yaw. It was a bit wambly. I think Johnny stamped suddenly. We were going more smoothly and the stick was central. We were in the air, rushing at some trees. They removed themselves without much assistance. I corrected another non-existent yaw, and we swung sideways. I was forgetting which foot was which. But we were over the wood and in the air.

This was Bernard's ET and we did a few banks and gliding turns. Unfortunately you can never hear in ET and I hadn't even got a helmet that fitted. Eventually Johnny had to point.

We did our landing together, Johnny screaming a running commentary which I couldn't hear at all. It was a very long glide, almost an overshoot. Then I took off again by myself, quite nicely, I thought. We came round again and I landed her alone. That is to say, I thought I did. Johnny certainly interfered. It wasn't nearly so difficult as I expected, and it is a curious fact that I do seem to see the ground and feel the wings beginning to stall by touch. I took off again, still in a kind of stupor, and Johnny took her round very quickly on a low raking bank. He handed her over to me, after side-slipping off some height, and I knew that this time I was really to do it by myself. I was all for it. Being in the air is extraordinary: one is too busy and interested to pay any attention to fear. I suppose I shall be afraid when I go solo, but meanwhile I can't whip up any horror at all, except by spinning. And this is only a physical horror, induced by one's tummy. In the aeroplane with Johnny I don't take the ground seriously. I found myself flying at it with a kind of happy insouciance.

When it seemed rather near I began to flatten out. But it was not near enough. I pointed myself at it again and flattened once more. This is called 'doing a Burton.' I was prepared to go on doing this till Doomsday, when Johnny said: 'Give her to me.' He pushed the throttle on, and, with the wheels almost touching the ground, we zoomed off over the wood.

Johnny said: 'Now you can land with me.' I realised miserably that we were to stop. I howled for just one more, but he pretended not to hear. Or actually didn't. When we were down he said: 'It's no good going on. I've been screaming myself hoarse. I wish that bloody JT would turn up. You must get your own helmet made. It's no good going on.' I begged in vain. He merely went away.

Johnny has an amazing knack of stopping at the critical moment, just when you think you have got the thing taped, and want one more go. I am sure this must be good for one.

JT turned up ten minutes later.

I like landing and feel confident about it. It is exhilarating, graceful and curiously remote from serious considerations.

I like taking off and thought it the more difficult of the two. This is because of my feud with the rudder bar.

To-morrow is a new day.

27. v. xxxiv.

The wind rose again, and blew in exactly the wrong kind of gust from the approximate west. I took Peter, and Johnny was an angel, giving him a lesson without his being a member of the club. My relations with Johnny are rather amusing, and have been considerably clarified by Peter. To begin with, I guessed almost at once that Johnny could not be trusted about times. So, when he begins trying to shuffle off the hour of my lesson, asking me: 'When have you got to be back?' I made a practice of deducting one hour from the real time. Yesterday Johnny said: 'When have you got to be back?' I said, with milk-innocent eyes: 'Six o'clock.' Peter said: 'Not till seven, surely?' Johnny crowed with delight. All I could do was to attack Peter. Now we understand each other.

Walking over to JT, Johnny said: 'It's too rough for landings.'

I said: 'Couldn't I just try?'

He said: 'You can try if you like, but you won't be able to do it. It's too gusty.'

'Then can I do spins?'

'You will have to do one with me first.'

'Can I do a vertical bank?'

'We'll see whether you do your other ones properly.'

I said: 'I hate your wretched banks. They're unethical and lousy.'

When Peter's lesson was over, we scrambled in. I said: 'Please may I take off?'

Johnny said: 'It will be difficult to-day. Landings too. You see, you won't know when you are doing it and when it is the air. But you may take off, if you like. I will be there to put you right.'

It is like being a baby in arms, or, worse still, a baby being held under the armpits and taught to walk. Johnny held me under the armpits, suggested the right moment for easing back the stick, corrected several yaws, and somehow, staggering horribly, we were in the air.

We flew and climbed. All the time I was getting into hot water for see-sawing the nose up and down. I watched the A.S.I. desperately, and it veered between 75 and 60. Whenever it went down to 60 Johnny swore. Whenever it went up to 75 he did the same. At 1,500 feet I realised what we were going to do. At 2,400 he asked the height and I said 2, 200. I looked gingerly over the side, and there was the earth, looking much too far away. There was a perfect ring of silver clouds all round the horizon, like the *rosa dei beati* in Dante. We were above them. Their startling and remote radiance edged off into a misty inner ring, which framed the very distant platter of each. I looked into the cockpit again for company.

At 3,000 Johnny said: 'Right-oh,' and explained all over again. JT lacks Handley Page slots and for some reason seemed to need holding up for her stall much less. This may have been an illusion. Anyway, I knew what was coming and suffered less in making up my mind to it. We fell over sideways with less of a surprise, and after less suspense. I was careful in looking at the earth, half contracting my eyes so as not to give it my full attention, whilst it spun gaily away at an incredible speed. It is funny looking straight down into the brown earthy bosom, much more surprising as it first appears, with the dive than later when it spins. One is so accustomed to horizons that it is a shock to find oneself without one. We did this spin together, and, as I pushed on right rudder, it was very satisfactory to find the fields slowing up. I was not giddy or sick. With the stick central we roared at the earth, and pulled the horizon back to view with happy deliberation.

Altitude 2,000.

Johnny chattered away about not coming out too fiercely, or one pulled off one's wings. Then to my horror he proposed another little one. I felt that 2,000 was rather inadequate, but supposed that he must know what he was after.

We spun again.

It was slower, less of it, and we came out after a tentative gyration.

Then we did banks and gliding turns, all inadequate. I am a fool with my nose on a gliding turn. To-day I was mud. I couldn't seem to get the right angle and Johnny didn't tell me. I must ask for another demonstration of this.

I am terrified of Johnny, as everybody is, but with a curious confiding terror. I was frightened in the same admiring and want-to-do-better-feeling way of Dap, who tried to teach me to fence at Cambridge. It is a question of being a door-mat for what you admire. The artist gets it given him. Johnny, of course, swears and raves like a trooper: but with a just detectable edge of kindness and decency which puts things right. Not always, however. He tells a nice story of a female pupil to whom he administered a more than usually vulgar and dumbfounding rebuke, whereupon she burst into tears, let go of the stick, and announced: "If you speak to me like that again *I won't try!*"

We did a landing together. So far as I could see I had nothing to do with it whatever, and all I can remember is the very-far-backness of the stick in my stomach.

I took off again. It was an incredibly tipsy affair, so staggering that it wasn't really clear when we first got into the air. Still, I was proud of being there at all.

We did a vertical bank for fun. Johnny did it, talking incessantly about things which I couldn't hear.

My banks were O.K. with the engine on, because Johnny's remark before we set out had made me angry enough to pay attention to them. I am afraid I am a lackadaisical airman. So long as I am in the air I like the aeroplane to wriggle and plunge and soar. After all, it is what birds do. Boring round in a perfectly executed circle, with the nose on the horizon, seems sadly unimaginative. However, Johnny had said the right thing to make me hug the wretched skyline like an automaton.

Gliding turns are much nicer. You soar and you are not tiresomely flat. My own gliding turns must be almost exciting for Johnny. They have a tendency to vary between stalls and spins.

I said: 'I am afraid I am going to feel depressed to-day, for the first time.'

Johnny said: 'Oh no, you won't.'

He took over, slipped off height with exquisite bravado, and landed with me. Again I clung hammily to various handles, hoping that I was doing something, listened to the encouraging voice, and found myself sitting on the earth with the stick in my tummy. It waggled about, hitting my legs. The rudder bars made coarse leaps, as if we were bicycling, and we taxied up to the sheds.

I did not want to get out.

I got out.

Bad.

I have only done two things to-day. I was allowed to swing Johnny's prop when he took off with Peter, and I remembered to rev up the engine as I switched off.

Afterwards we stayed to watch. An experienced pilot went off alone with JT and did complete rolls. This is quite the happiest manoeuvre I have seen. It is a quick sheer movement of *joie de vivre*, far more effective than the loop or the ungainly spin. Peter said: 'What a lovely man! He *is* enjoying himself.'

I asked how many revolutions we had gone in our thousand-foot spin. If he had said 50 I should not have been surprised, though 30 would have been nearer my guess. The actual number was 3 or 4.

Then the yellow peril* went and did curley-cues, but nothing so lovely as the horizontal pleasure-spins which JT had been indulging in, like a sky fish rolling over its own axis, belly upwards for a second, out of happy love.

I got home in 33 minutes, from door to door. Yesterday, when I was in a raging temper, I reached Farmer Williams' turning in half an hour exactly.

Went on a teetotal pub crawl with Ker and the Beam. At the Queen's Arms at Ferneley there were some rather

*An Avro Tutor painted yellow.

happy men arguing about a trick in which four persons, using only their forefingers, lifted another man in a chair. This was alleged to be much easier if you all put your hands on his head first, left hands starting. We did this to all the fattest men in the pub: quite a sensible pastime.

Coming home we heard a nightingale, and listened to him for about ten minutes: he was a bit squeaky.

Funnily enough, my happiest days seem to be my worst flying ones.

I asked Johnny whether I had taken off by myself that second time, as I thought I had. He said: 'No.'

But still, it was a happy day.

28. v. xxxiv.

I know every bend in the road now, to Credon. I have to drive fifty miles a day for my flying. It is not a thrilling stretch historically, except when you cross the great Roman road at Cester, because of the usual meiosis of the Shire. At Milton Malsor there lived, contemporaneous with Shakespeare's character, a man called Bardolph. It would be nice to think that there was some connection with that nose. And at the Abbey, which I leave on my right, there was once a prior called William who, in spite of twice being suspended by the archbishop, persisted, to his final degradation into the ranks of the ordinary monks, in entertaining young ladies in the orchard.

There is a firm streak of decency in the Shire.

29. v. xxxiv.

To-day was cruel. I fled over after luncheon and found Johnny ready by 2.30. There was scarcely any wind, just a small stir from the west. I was taught to taxi, a vulgar business in which one bangs the rudder bar and uses the ailerons in an opposite sense. Neither difficult nor inspiring. It is easier to turn to the left than to the right.

I see no reason why I should describe the whole débacle. We did take-offs and landings incessantly for about an hour (my first lesson of more than 20 or 30 minutes) and not one decent one. Taking-off I stagger into the air like a lunatic, wagging my tail and pointing to all points of the compass. Is this because Johnny has frightened me about my tail unduly? I think it is more because (*a*) I begin to correct before anything is needed, (*b*) I continue correcting imaginary wags after the tail is up. (N.B.—Ask Johnny whether correction is much needed after the tail is up. Perhaps this is the trouble.) (*c*) I correct perhaps too quickly. If I allowed the fault to develop just a little more I would then be sure that it was a fault and be more collected in dealing with it. I am inclined to think that I must take my tail less seriously, at any rate, as soon as it is off the ground,★ and give myself more time and caution in coping with it.

I did one decent take-off. This was after a simply terrible one. The moment we were in the air Johnny grabbed the machine, hopped the hedge, forced-landed in the next field, and made me take-off again. This little surprise was a success.

My landings were moderate in respect of height, but suffered from an inability to put the tail hard down at the last moment. As far as I can see, you have to coax your stall with prodigious gentleness till you are flying level at the right height, a few inches off the ground, and losing speed. This gentleness seems to give way at the last moment to quite a coarse and abrupt squat, with the stick right back in the belly. By failing to achieve this last action I provided a series of quite exciting wheel landings, in one of which we actually leapt into the air, throttled on and flew away again.

I felt like mud, but I can't help feeling that Johnny had

★Later——?

put me wrong initially, by something he said or omitted to say.

Some of the testimonials which I shall always be able to look back upon were: 'I have never had a pupil who wags his tail so much or so unnecessarily on the take-off,' and 'You would have thought that a bloody fool could do it.'

We landed in the middle of the lesson, whilst Johnny went away to cool his ire. I sat in the cockpit and merely wondered. I have a sort of apathy at dual with Johnny. I enjoy it so much, and like looking back at my tail following me through the air.

When he came back, he had dropped the indignant approach. It was infinitely worse when he was exuding comfort and reassurance.

I hope I shall do better next time, and think I will. My gliding turns are still dangerous. Please God, help me to remember to keep my nose at the gliding angle: to take my tail less seriously at the take-off: to make up my mind about that last movement of the stick on landing, because theoretically it ought all to be as gentle as thistledown: and to remember to navigate her once she is on the ground.

Independence—a state of being self-contained—is the only generosity, I thought, the only charity we can claim of a living creature. We must have nothing to do with another's bones; that is our only right—to have nothing to do with them. The bone must be the axis of a globe of intrusion-proof glass. One could not say, watching a hawk: 'I ought perhaps to do this for him.' Therefore, not only is he safe from me, but I am safe from him.

STELLA BENSON

3. vi. xxxiv.

The snakes are about again. Last year I used to go out with Hughesdon to catch them, and then turn them loose in the sitting-room. At one time I had about a dozen. There are four in the room just now.

Grass snakes are fascinating pets. It is impossible to impose upon them, or to steal their affections, or to degrade either party in any way. They are always inevitably themselves, and with a separate silurian beauty. The plates of the jaw are fixed in an antediluvian irony. They move with silence, unless in crackling grass or with a scaly rustle over a wooden floor, pouring themselves over obstacles and round them. They are inquisitive. They live loose in the room, except that I lock them up at nights so that the maids can clean in the mornings without being frightened. The big open fireplace is full of moss and ferns, and there is an aquarium full of water in which they can soak themselves if they wish. But mostly they prefer to lie under the hot pipes of the radiator, or to burrow inside the sofa. We had to perform a Caesarian operation on the sofa last year, to get out a big male.

It is nice to come into the room and look quickly round it, to see what they are doing. Perhaps there is one behind Aldous Huxley on the book-shelves, and it is always worth moving the left-hand settle away from the wall. One of them has a passion for this place and generally falls out. Another meditates all day in the aquarium, and the fourth lives in the moss.

Or it is nice to be working in the arm-chair, and to look up suddenly at an imagined sound. A female is pouring from behind the sofa. As the floor is of polished wood she gets a poor grip of it (she prefers the sheepskin hearth-rug) and elects to decant herself along the angle between wall and floor. Here she can press sideways as well as downwards, and gets a better grip.

She saw our movement as we looked up, and now stops dead, her head raised in curiosity. Her perfect forked tongue flickers blackly out of its specially armoured hole (like the hole for the starting handle in a motor, but constructed so as to close itself when not in use) and waves itself like lightning in our direction. It is what she feels with in front of her, her testing antennae, and this is her mark of interrogation. An emphatic movement: she can't reach us, but she is thinking Who or What? And so the tongue comes out. We sit quite still.

The tongue comes out two or three times (its touch on the hand is as delicate as the touch of a butterfly) and flickers in the air. It is a beautiful movement, with more down in it than up. It can be faintly reproduced by waggling the bent forefinger quickly in a vertical plane. Then she goes on with her pour, satisfied, towards her objective in the moss. We sit as still as a mouse.

I try to handle these creatures as little as possible. I do not want to steal them from themselves by making them pets. The exchange of hearts would degrade both of us. It is only that they are nice. Nice to see the strange wild things loose, living their ancient unpredictable lives with such grace. They are more ancient than the mammoth, and infinitely more beautiful. They are dry, cool and strong. The fitting and variation of the plates, the lovely colouring, the movement, their few thoughts: one could meditate upon them like a jeweller for months.

It is exciting to catch them. You go to a good wood, and look for snaky places in it. It is difficult to define these. There has to be undergrowth, but not overgrowth: a sunny patch, a glade or tiny clearing in the trees: perhaps long grass and a bit of moss, but not too wet. You go into it and there is a rustle. You can see nothing, but dive straight at the sound. You see just a few inches of the back, deceptively fluid for catching hold of, as it flashes from side to side. You must pounce on it at once, for there is no time to think, holding it down or grabbing it by head or tail or anywhere. There is no time to select. This is always exciting to me, because I frighten myself by thinking that it might be an adder. As a matter of fact, there are very few adders in the Shire, and in any case they move differently. An adder would strike back at you, I suppose, but a grass snake does not. It pretends to strike, with mouth wide open and the most formidable-looking fangs; but it stops its head within a millimetre of the threatened spot, a piece of bluff merely.

When you have grabbed your snake, you pick it up. Instantly it curls round your hand and arm, hissing and lunging at you with the almost obtuse angle of its jaw; exuding a white fluid from its vent, which has a metallic stink like acetylene. Take no notice of it at all. Like an efficient governess with a refractory child, you speak sharply to the smelly creature and hold it firmly. You take hold of its tail, unwind it, roll it in a ball (it is wriggling so much that it generally helps in this), tie it up in your handkerchief, put it in your trouser pocket and look for another.

When you loose it in your sitting-room it rushes off along the floor, swishing frantically but making little progress on the polished wood, and conceals itself in the darkest corner. At night, when you come to lock it up, it makes a fuss. It produces the smell again, and the hiss. In the morning it is the same. Next night perhaps the smell is omitted, or fainter. In a few days there is only a dim hiss, a kind of grumble. This goes as well, until there is only a gentle protesting undulation as it is lifted off the ground.

I remember particularly two of last year's snakes. One was a baby male (the yellow markings are brighter in the male) only about eight inches long. He was a confiding snake, and I once took him to church in my pocket, to make him a Christian and to comfort me during the sermon. I hope it was not an undue interference with his life: I never carried him about like that again, he seemed to like the warmth of my pocket, and I believe he did not change his creed.

Talking of Christians, I never christened the snakes. To have called them names would have been ridiculous, as it is with cars. A snake cannot have a name. If it had to be addressed I suppose it would be addressed by its generic title: Snake.

The other one, I regret to say, was nearly a pet. She was a well-grown female with a scar on her neck. I suppose this had been done to her by man. It was the scar that first attracted me to her, or rather made me take special notice of her, because she was easy to distinguish. I soon found that when the time came for putting her to bed she did not undulate. She never troubled to conceal herself at bed-time, nor to slide away from me when I approached. She would crawl right up to me, and pour over my feet while I was working. There was no horrible affection or prostration; only she was not afraid of me. She went over my feet because they were in a direct line with the place she was making for. She trusted, or at least was indifferent.

It was a temptation. One coldish afternoon she was sitting in my chair when I wanted to read. I picked her up and put her in my lap. She was not particularly comfortable, and began to go away. I held her gently by the tail. She decided that it was not worth a scene, and stayed. I put my free hand over her, and she curled up beneath it, the head sticking out between two fingers and the tongue flickering every now and then, when a thought of curiosity entered her slow, free mind.

After that I used sometimes to sit with my two hands cupped, and she would curl between them on cold days. My hands were warm, that was all.

It was not quite all. I am afraid a hideous tinge of

possession is creeping into this account. When other people came into the room she used to hiss. I would be dozing with her tight, dry coils between my palms, and there would be a hiss. The door would have opened and somebody would have come in. Or again, if I showed her to people she would hiss at them. If they tried to catch her, she would pour away. But when I gave her to them she was quiet.

I think I succeeded in keeping my distance. At any rate, she had a love affair with one of the males. I remember finding them coiled together on the corner table: a double rope-coil of snake which looked like a single one, except that it had two heads. I did not realise that this was an affair of the heart, at the time.

Later on she began to look ill. She was lumpy and flaccid. I became worried about the commissariat. Snakes rarely eat—seldom more than once a fortnight—but when they do eat they are particular. The staple food is a live frog, swallowed alive and whole. Anybody who has ever kept snakes will know how difficult it is to find a frog. The whole of the Shire seems to be populated by toads: one can scarcely move without treading on a toad: but toads disagree with snakes. They exude something from the skin.

I had been short of frogs lately, and (as I merely kept them loose in the aquarium so that the snakes could help themselves when they wanted) did not know when she had last had a meal. I thought I was starving her and became agitated. I spent hours looking for frogs, and found one eventually, but she wouldn't touch it. I tried a gold-fish, but that was no good either. She got worse. I was afraid she was poisoned, or melancholic from her unnatural surroundings.

Then came the proud day. I got back at half-past twelve, and looked for her on the hearth-rug, but she was not there. She was in the aquarium, sunlit from the french windows. Not only she. I went closer and looked. There were twenty-eight eggs.

Poor old lady, she was in a dreadful state. Quite apathetic and powerless, she could scarcely lift her head. Her body had fallen in on itself, leaving two ridges, as if she were quite a slim snake dressed in clothes too big for her. When I picked her up she hung limp, as if she were actually dead; but her tongue flickered. I didn't know what to do.

I got a gold-fish bowl and half-filled it with fresh grass clippings. I put her in it, with the frog, and tied paper over the top as if it were a jam jar. I made holes in the paper and took it out on to the lawn, in the full glare of the summer sun. Snakes are woken up by heat, and the bowl would concentrate the sun's beams. It was all I could think of or do, before I went in to lunch.

I came back in half an hour. The bowl was warm with moisture, the grass clippings were browning, the frog was gone; and inside was Matilda (she positively deserved a name) as fit as a flea and twice as frisky.

4. vi. xxxiv.

The scarred snake may have been a good mistress, but she was a bad mother. If she had known anything about maternity, she would not have laid her eggs in the aquarium. It seems that water is one of the things that is fatal to the eggs of grass snakes. I picked them out, and put them in another gold-fish bowl, this time full of grass clippings that were already rotten. Then I left them in the sun. They only went mouldy.

She was completely tame, and the inevitable happened. The time came for me to go away for two months, so I gave her her liberty. I took her out into the fountain court (next time it shall be into the deepest and most unpopulated forest) and put her on the ground in the strong July sunlight. She was delighted by it, and pleased to go. I watched her to-froing away, till she slipped into the angle of a flower-bed, and then went resolutely indoors. There were plenty of other things in the future besides grass snakes.

That night I went down to the lake to bathe, and stepped over a dead snake in the moonlight. I guessed before I looked for the scar. I had kept my distance successfully, so that there were no regrets at parting, but I had destroyed a natural balance. She had lost her bitter fear of man: a thing which it is not wise to lose.

I feel some difficulty in putting this properly. Some bloody-minded human being had come across her on a path, and gone for her with a stick. She was harmless, useless dead, very beautiful, easy prey. He slaughtered her with a stick, and grass snakes are not easy to kill. It is easy to maim them, to bash them on the head until the bones are pulp. The lower jaw no longer articulates with the upper one, but lies sideways under the crushed skull, shewing the beautiful colours of its unprotected inner side. The whole reserved face suddenly looks pitiful, because it has been spoilt and ravaged. The black tongue makes a feeble flicker still.

These things had been done, to a creature which was offering confidence, with wanton savagery. Why? Why the waste of beauty and the degradation to the murderer himself? He was not creating a beauty by destroying this one. He cannot even have considered himself clever.

5. vi. xxxiv.

The wind has been gusty again and landing practice, for me, impossible. If only it would rain when it's windy, and be sunny at other times, one would find it easier to believe in providence. As it is, the exceptional English drought continues, and without even helping the air-minded. To-day, however, the wind was steady and not very strong. It blew more or less from the N.E., and one was landing across the sheds. When I arrived for a lesson at 2.45 Johnny was just off to fetch Mrs. Bernard. So the lesson didn't take place till about 3.20. Just as I drew up a man was landing ET, and Johnny said in the voice of a proud but faintly anxious father: 'This is his second solo.' We watched him narrowly. He made a 3-point landing, and Johnny said: 'There; not much wrong with that, was there?' It was an interesting moment.

Whilst Johnny was away for Mrs. Bernard I watched a woman, who has flown 60 hours solo, practising landings, etc., with JT. She was rather a nice woman, but she was inclined to do a Burton and to give herself plenty of room over the hedge. Once she looped (or so she said afterwards, but I wasn't looking) and once she spun. This spin was instructive to watch. It is obviously quite true that JT spins more easily than ET, but it was also interesting to see that spins can vary. I am sure hers must have been a much *looser* spin than Johnny's, with the tail making a much wider arc round the axis, for she did at least five turns in only so many hundred feet. It was quite pretty after all.

When Johnny came back we went off quickly. My new helmet, i.e. my first own one, was not very good acoustically. I told him that I should never learn anything actually during a lesson, but it would crystallise afterwards. Then I took off, I think much more than less alone. I had determined to pay less attention to my tail and incidentally to keep up a tiny paddling movement on the rudder bars all the time, so as to be more in touch with them; or rather what they call in the slips 'more on my toes.' This worked and by the end of my half-hour Johnny said: 'Two of your take-offs were very nearly perfect, and I think you have got them taped, haven't you?'

Landings were bouncy, and gliding turns at an admirable angle (60—70 A.S.I.) but inclined to go on too long. I must remember to come out of my turn long before I am at the point when I want to leave it.

Johnny said: 'Now take-off yourself, come round in your own time, and do your own landing.'

We came safely unstuck and it was grand to be able to

sweep round as one wanted to, without having to pay attention to tiresome orders: 'Now to the left: don't yaw: don't climb: keep her straight: now to the left,' etc., etc., etc.

I took her where I wanted her, switched off on my own initiative, did a reasonable gliding turn, and began to come in to the west of the sheds. I saw that we were going to undershoot and gave her a second or two of engine. Johnny forcibly put the nose down after this, as I switched off. I think it was the only time he touched her. We did a bit of a Burton, very slight, and landed with a bounce.

Johnny said: 'If you find you are going to undershoot, switch on and go right round again. This is important. If you give her a small burst of engine and try to make the field you (did I get this right?) drop your nose as you switch off and are liable to stall.' I will do as he says, but I don't see why, and am certain that somebody who really could fly would use engine and come in perfectly safely.

I now developed a curious trait, indistinguishable to myself but highly exacerbating to Johnny. I began flying with my right wing down. Johnny swore and raved: in vain. It continued, so he said, to be down. I looked at it a good deal, but it seemed all right to me. One felt as if he were commenting on a natural infirmity, like a club foot or cross eyes. A sort of baffled and unhappy wonder, as if one were a penguin with asymmetrical flippers. On my last take-off it was alleged to be practically trailing along the ground. Johnny has a nice habit of smacking his stick with the flat of his hand, in the desired direction, as if he were a she-bear correcting her young. I did not know of this habit till afterwards. When we were about 10 feet off the ground, with the wing (alleged) at an angle of 30 degrees, he smacked the stick to the left. It shot out of my hand and disappeared into the recesses of the cockpit. I thought he had taken over and only felt for it in a leisurely way. I dare say we must have flown for seconds, at ten feet, with neither of us touching either of the sticks.

My landings are still babyish, but they are beginning to crystallise, and I hope I shall be able to remember the take-off.

On the way home I gave three college yells for myself and did the standing start from door to door in 35 minutes, although every traffic light in Middlehampton was against us, and argued all the way.

6. vi. xxxiv.

A bumpy day. I suppose I must have done, at most, six circuits, with take-offs and landings. Only it is so difficult to remember things like this precisely. One is conscious only of the actual moment in hand, acutely wrapped up in it, and afterwards the thing seems a daze, an ocean of contiguous moments with a few island peaks. I did these by myself, having the machine taken from me, I think, twice, at the moment of turning to glide in, because I had misjudged my distance. Perhaps more than twice. But only for a second or two, and once on landing. Probably more. One is incurably optimistic. Probably more. Anyway, I did well.

My take-offs were obviously my own, and all un-waggly but one. Once I waggled, and once I climbed a bit too steeply. But Johnny touched nothing.

My landings were at any rate effective. That is to say, one reached and remained eventually stationary upon the ground. Once Johnny, I fear, pulled the stick back because we were landing on an uphill slope at the east end, by the hedge. (Wind abating and from N.W.) Once, at a biggish bounce, he gave her, for some unknown reason, a burst of engine. I have an idea that he meant to bounce off and go right round again, but I stalled her firmly, and he abandoned the project on the instant. This idea is probably incorrect. So it seems that he interfered with my landings twice.

Never mind. On the last circuit I took off unreproached, came round to my mark in my own time, cut off, did a superb gliding turn and landed, if with a bouncer, at least alive. *During this circuit Johnny did not speak, except to say that the machine was my own.* Rapture.

You see, the speaking is a brake upon one's achievement. How can one say that one is landing, when Johnny's voice is all the time coaxing a wing, holding her off, and urging the psychological moment? But once, on a whole circuit (but on second thoughts, it was interfered with, it must have been), my landing was all my own. Reduce it then to this definitely: on one circuit I took off, placed myself, cut off, glided in, in silence. I think he must have spoken as I touched. Anyway it was a bounce. The silent part was perfect.

My right wing is still maimed. A cross between *ses ailes de géant l'empêchent de marcher* and 'which, like a wounded snake, drags its slow length along.' The stick got several slaps.

I must try next time (*a*) to cope with this wing and consciously fly left wing down, (*b*) to hold off my landings less forcibly (I am inclined to go up again), (*c*) not to put my tail up quite so high in taking off.

There are several jewels for my crown to-day. Johnny, after my third landing, said: 'You got the feel of her that time, didn't you?' in quite an excited voice. I fervently agreed. At tea afterwards he said: 'Never mind. Young Tim wasn't so bad to-day. I haven't quite given him up for lost.' It was lovely.

One of his better remarks in the air was: 'Don't be so strong. No good being a strong man in the air. In bed, yes; but in the air, no good at all.' Another: 'If you land across wind like that on a windy day, you'll get a gust and go right over. Then where will you be? Where shall I be? Both of us: gone to——'

To-day it was the new club machine—AV or something like that. The exhaust leaks and is unpleasant. The cheese cutter could almost be left central all the time, and seems happiest when only used over one-third of its arc.

I am flying well.

7. *vi. xxxiv.*

Pets are almost always fatal, to oneself or to them. It is the curse of possession or motherhood. Mothers ruin their children, choke them like ivy. Dog-lovers steal the souls of their dogs and lose something in exchange. There is an essay on this subject by (I think) Stella Benson, called 'A Firefly to Steer By.' Everybody ought to read it.

On the other hand, I don't think there is anything wrong with independent alliance. A hedgehog which lives its own life in the garden, but will come for bread and milk when called, is a decent creature. He gets his milk, and I get the pleasure of watching his queer ways. It is a fair and irresponsible exchange. The unfledged sparrows, which I have tried to rear, fallen from spring nests, have always been a failure. For one thing, they invariably died. But it would have been worse if they had lived. I had a tame chicken when I was tiny, that used to regard me as its mother. It used to cheep and flutter, for me to hold my cupped hand about an inch off the ground. When I did, it would butt its way underneath, and cheep and go to sleep. It grew up, and lost its need for mothers, and nearly broke my heart. Horrible.

This is why I tried a cat. Cats are said to be independent, and Siamese cats in particular are said to be brave. Chatterly is a female Siamese cat, whose mate, Chatsworth, belongs to Ker. They smell, and are a damned nuisance to feed (being hideously voracious for raw meat), and Ker is fastidious and idle: so they both live in my room.

I have made a practice, from their earliest kittenhood, of training them to place no reliance or affection upon anybody but themselves. In vain. Chatsworth is an arrant

coward, and Chatterly practically an idiot. They were
both chased, at an early age, by the night watchman's dog;
and this seems to have had a bad effect on their
psychology. Far from wandering free and independent, as
I should like them to do, they sleep all day in the sitting-
room, in the intervals of mewing at me for more food. The
mew of a Siamese cat is the most piercing thing I know,
and they eat about two pounds each of raw meat every
day. Worm powders increase their appetite.

The worst aspect of their invasion is that which bears
upon the snakes. In order to keep the snakes inside the
room, I have to stick a sheet of brown paper over the
bottom of the french window with drawing pins. There is
a slight give in it, and this generally prevents the snakes
from getting out. It also prevents the cats from getting
out. House trained as they are, I can scarcely be angry in
this case if their modesty breaks down.

8. vi. xxxiv.

These cats are the bane of my existence. I never seem
able to get away, because they have to be fed twice a day,
and now I have to lose the snakes. It boiled down to a
choice between the two; and as the cats might produce a
litter of kittens which could be sold at two guineas each,
avarice triumphed. So now life has to be feline and smelly.
The responsibility is the worst part.

Last summer the ménage was a happy one. There were
not only the snakes, but the toads. Every now and then, in
the desperate search for frogs, I used to lose patience and
bring home a toad. Subconsciously I must have felt that if
the snakes were really starving they would probably give
in and have a toad after all.

There is something nice about toads. Their texture to
the hand is less pleasant than that of the snake: not because
they are slimy, but because they are less compact and seem
colder. They are, however, amusing companions. Unlike

the frog (who has the mentality of a chicken or a maiden aunt), the toad takes life as it comes. He sits in the middle of the carpet and reflects upon it. If you disturb his meditations by coming too near, he hops slowly away in a series of tedious and audible bounds, landing with the whole of his under-carriage at once. His stomach slaps the floor. The Beam, who as an intelligent person does not notice his feet, once trod on a toad without doing it any harm. They are resilient.

I was sitting in my chair last year, reading, when one of the snakes came out from behind the sofa. The snakes always made their way round the room in the angle between wall and floor, which meant that they had a poor field of vision when coming round a series of projecting corners by the fireplace. A toad was sitting round the next corner that the snake was due to take. Each was unaware of the other. The toad was obviously deep in thought.

When the snake came round the corner, they both got a shock. The snake paused and began flickering with its tongue. I thought it had a rather baleful expression in its eye. The toad slowly raised its body to the full extent of its legs and faced the snake. It was no longer a sitting toad, but a toad on four legs, like a horse. Only its bottom stuck in the air. It began to swell, and at the same time lowered its head in a deep salaam as if it were doing press-ups. It was now a back-to-front toad, its body at least half as fat again, its head on the ground, and its apex at the back. It remained motionless.

The snake made up its mind and continued to advance. Unfortunately the toad was also in the angle of the wall, in the direct line of passage. The snake reached the toad and touched it with its head. The toad froze perceptibly. Then the snake walked over it. Slowly, remorselessly, it poured itself up and over. The body became narrower, the tail passed. The toad continued to hold up its bottom. The snake was rustling in the fireplace moss. The toad began to deflate, relaxed its hind legs, came to anchor on the earth

again as if it were an airship mooring at Cardington. It
ruminated on the experience. The gullet of its throat beat
regularly in and out.

I believe that one of my toads was once eaten. I used to
put the snakes away for the night in a round apple basket,
half a bushel, with straw in it and moss. This I kept in a big
cupboard with sliding doors, and the snakes often slept
outside the actual basket. One night, when I was putting
them away, I got more than usually agitated about
whether they were having enough to eat. I bethought
myself of a small toad, no more than the size of a frog,
whom I had carried in that day. He was evidently a very
young and inexperienced toad, about in the prep. school
stage, and perhaps he would have too small a supply of
sweating venom or be the right size to be eaten. I put him
into the basket.

It was a heart-rending affair, really. I put him straight
down on a snake's back, and the poor little fellow stiffened
just like a human being. 'My God!' he said, and his hair
stood on end, and his bones turned to water. Then, with a
horrible pathos, he tiptoed off towards the side of the
basket. He moved laboriously, in extreme terror. You
could see him thinking: 'Hush, I must be quiet; perhaps I
can get away before they notice, if I am as quiet as a
mouse.' He reached the side, but it was too high. He stood
erect against it, too human for words, and weakly pawed
the wall. The snakes rattled in the straw.

I said to myself that nature was like this, and the snakes
might starve. I shut the cupboard and went to bed. I got so
far as to put on my dressing-gown, after midnight, with
the intention of a relenting rescue. But nature was like this.
In the morning I got up at six and hurried down. He was
gone.

There is no intrinsic reason why one should not keep
adders as pets, nor is there much reason why they should
be destroyed in the open when met. Their venom is defen-
sive. It would mean handling them with leather gloves in

the angry early stages, and the moment when you changed from leather to bare hands might be exciting. Otherwise they would be delightful.

The objection is that they would be prone to bite one's friends: a purely legal objection, in some cases.

9. vi. xxxiv.

To-day was bad, or only very moderate. I am a long, long way off going solo, though everybody is beginning very kindly to tell me about it. 'This is our next solo,' they say to each other, introducing me in all directions. It is not yet an intimidating thought, because, like everything so far to do with flying, quite beyond the bounds of specu-lation. Still, I see a nasty double-entendre in Johnny's eye, and to-day he asked me whether Ker had done his solo yet. Ker, of course, joined a much more fashionable club than mine. This might mean that he has solos dimly in mind with regard to me, and it impressed me suitably.

The wind was practically a dead calm. My take-offs were shaky, and the one really smooth one served to shew up the others. The landings were goodish in point of judging the come-in. There was one three-pointer. The others were bouncy, but not terrible, except the last, when I throttled on and flew away again. The wind being so very absent made it necessary to hold off with patience. Much, much waiting, and a feeling of lack of wind under the wings to judge the stall by. Johnny's voice slightly bothers me. I don't quite see how, unless he is flying the machine, he can feel the right moment to say Now. Doubtful query: Am I brave enough to take no notice of his directions next time and land as I think it ought to be done?

I liked looking down at another machine, 500 feet below, taking slowly off. Garnett's description of this is perfect.

After I had throttled on from my last bounce Johnny asked for the controls, came round in the aerodrome itself, and landed with the most perfect side-slip to within about six inches of the ground. It was dazzling: wildly virile and beautiful. He threw her, sawed her, slewed her edgeways through the air.

I must remember.

The long hold off on windless days.

To throttle *full* on at take off.

To see that the throttle is *right* back when landing.

To-day it was JT, and everybody was carrying lots of hay about on their tail skids. Flying is making me forget about harvests.

An aeroplane turned up to-day that had been establishing a lot of records. It had the places it had been to, from Iceland to India, painted with the distances on its sides. We all went about, muttering to each other about showing off. But, after all, why not? If I had an aeroplane that had flown to Iceland, I should certainly write REJKAVIK on its sides—probably all over. It looked ornamental, it must have been pleasantly reminiscent, and the achievement was genuine. Instead of criticising this aeronaut, we would have done better to be flying to Rejkavik ourselves.

Yesterday the Prince of Wales landed to open an agricultural show at Kindle. His signature was in the visitor's book.

10. vi. xxxiv.

An unsatisfactory day. I got over there by ten o'clock and booked two lessons, one for the morning and one for the afternoon. I had to wait about an hour for the first, and spent the time lying on my back in the strong sun, talking. The people at Credon are nice. There is Ian, a little Scotsman with a very grubby face and false teeth, which he keeps on a nail in the workshops. He is after a B licence, and improves his mind between times by reading novels with profound concentration. His trait as an airman is to find always something worth complaint. Always either 'verra bumpy near the ground,' or 'nae wind for landing, or 'visibility deeficult.' He is good. The other B licence candidate is called something like Raymond, but not that. He also is charming, with black hair and protruding ears. Of the five of us who were talking, three had vivid ears, and only one was normal. Now what light does this throw on flying? Richmond, or whatever his name is, was at Bedale's. He is efficient, pleasant, a good mixer—but with that curious lack of aggression which seems to come from Bedale's.

The other two were pilots of only 2-4 hours' standing: hence junior to me, and faintly polite, which was amusing. One was bouncy, in a juvenile way, which was for that reason not unpleasant. The other, the widest-eared of the party, had been an observer during the war. We talked about Handley Page slots, and thence to crashes. He had seen a man crash in telegraph wires and then fry. I said, and felt, that I might have liked to see this. He said: 'No, you wouldn't, because he screamed as he fried.' Also he had seen, in his own diamond formation of bombers, a direct hit by an anti-aircraft gun. The machine turned completely over and they landed, wing to wing, on the machine behind it. They went down in a flat spin and broke up in the air. Observers, he said, were curiously treated in the war. His C.O. used to go round the squadron before every show, and shake hands with every pilot. After every show the proceeding was repeated with congratulations. He never spoke to an observer at all, unless he was mortally wounded.

Johnny was ready at last, and we did half an hour of landings in AV. I am confident of my take-offs and fairly certain that I should get down *alive* if I were allowed to go solo to-day. I am also quite certain that I should bounce. Johnny sat silent to-day, leaving it to me. I bounce because I come in too fast. So it is really a question of judging the approach in order to get the smooth, gentle, almost stalling glide, which doesn't so much need to be flattened out

too appreciably. This is badly explained. I ought to do
this ⁓⁓⁓⁓⁓ rather than this ⁓⁓⁓⁓.
It is a question of smooth, controlled approach.

Johnny's remarks to-day were excellent. To one person
he said: 'Don't be so timid. Treat her as you would treat a
passionate Spanish beauty.' He proceeded to stamp on the
rudder bars. To me, after a landing which contrived at the
very last thousandth of a second to put its tail down, he
announced: 'Well, that was born in the vestry.' I didn't
understand at once.

When we had finished I felt dumb. It was that timing of
the tail. My landings seemed destined for ever to be wheel
landings, a prospect of dreary stupidity.

We had lunch.

At about 3 Johnny took me again. Just the same. After
four circuits he saw somebody on the ground that he
wanted to talk to, and came in. He said: 'Do you mind if
we finish this later?' I said no.

Lying in the sun half an hour afterwards somebody (the
film scenario writer) said: 'I see you've had two lessons of
30 minutes to-day.' I went to see, and found that the
blasted little ground mechanic had entered it so.
Apparently he has been doing this all the time. Whenever
he sees me going off with Johnny he automatically puts me
down for 30 minutes. As most of my lessons have been of
20 minutes, this is a bad show. It not only costs me
money, but will make my log-book tell against me in
the Ker bet as to which of us goes solo in the least time.
Damn! I gave the mechanic a stony, and Johnny told him
off. This means I shall have to keep an eye on him in
future.

For the rest of the day, till 8 p.m., I hung about without
getting the lesson finished. Everybody was very busy.
The scenario writer and his wife, who both also hover on
the solo line, and were both also cheated of their second
lessons, were angry, too. I suppose Johnny ought to have
an assistant. He has flown eight hours a day this week.

An amusing thing happened this morning. An actor who is playing the lead in a flying play which is to be produced next week in London, came down, paid four guineas entrance fee, borrowed a helmet, and was photographed in JT, presumably about to take off. Two wenches stood and waved. The 4-hour man, the ex-observer, dressed up as Johnny (who happened to be in the air with me) and sat in the front cockpit for the picture. Then the aviator got out again and went back to London. A small piquancy is added to this anecdote by the fact that JT had broken a longeron, and was therefore, suitably enough, incapable of flight.

12. vi. xxxiv.

I found out to-day that a small strip, half a hide or something, at Credon, belonged to a niece of William the Conqueror. It is in such circles that we fly. Hers is a name which keeps cropping up in the northern parts of what I call the Shire, and she does not deserve lightly to be forgotten. Her uncle married her to Earl Waltheof, who was a son to no less a person than the Old Siward of Macbeth. He was not the one who died with all his wounds before, poor fellow; but he was an important personage under the old regime, none the less, and it was worth the Conqueror's while to conciliate him. Waltheof was confirmed Earl of Middlehampton before being given the Conqueror's niece in marriage. It seems that Judith was a person with a mind of her own. A contemporary monk, called Ingulphus, went so far as to describe her as *impiisima Jezebel*. She tempted her husband into conspiracy against the King, and then betrayed him. He was beheaded at Winchester in 1076, his dead body being insulted and buried at a cross-road.

Judith was next asked to marry Simon de St. Liz. She had done away with her first husband, possibly on account of a love affair somewhere, and anyway St. Liz had bandy legs. So she mutinied at the second political marriage, and William, angry, gave all her possessions as a dowry for her daughter Maude, who had to marry St. Liz in default of her mamma. Thus everybody except Waltheof was happy.

It is an interesting little fact that Waltheof was the first recorded person to be beheaded in this kingdom, and that the Shire also possesses among her alumni the last person to be gibbeted. The gibbet stood for a long time, until the skeleton fell off (he was a chimney sweep who murdered his victim by climbing down the chimney) and then a farmer bought it. He made a gate out of it, for one of his fields.

13. vi. xxxiv.

To-day was almost too poignant for record. Johnny took me in AV. Before we started, the scenario man informed me that it was bumpy. The aerodrome, he pointed out, was covered with people making hay, into the bargain, and a lesson was practically a waste of time. He is himself waiting to go solo, his nice film-star wife, Nell, having done it last Sunday, after I left, in 12 hours. I was miserable about other things, pretty fit and pretty ready to cope with bumps out of a sort of desperation.

I did half a dozen perfectly good landings—wheel landings, but without bounce: a speciality of mine. Johnny suddenly, hideously, said: 'Do another good circuit and I get out.'

My heart went absolutely into my belly.

With Johnny there it is all right, because one knows that if one isn't doing it properly he will say. I knew in my heart that I was incapable of doing my stuff alone.

Or did it rise into my larynx? Anyway, it swelled; and I forgot to put the cheese-cutter forward with engine on. Result: two circuits which were fights with the stick all the time, and in both I had to throttle on without landing.

Then I remembered the cheese-cutter.

Then I did my first perfect three-pointer.

Johnny said: 'You can fly all your bloody life without doing a better landing than that.'

He undid himself, got out, and went to look at the tail skid.

He held up the back of the machine.

I was in a kind of stupor.

He said: 'The spring is bust and has gone through the three-ply. We shall have to walk back. What a pity! I had already taken off my telephone to get out and send you solo.'

I walked back with him.

I can't say what I felt like. There was a great deal of satisfaction, which was not exactly relief, and a bemused feeling.

I said: 'I can stay all night, if you think there is a hope of getting me unstuck.'

If only one could define one's feelings. Tea was a whirligig of them. I wanted to do my solo, because Ker says he will do his to-day (though he has more hours), and because I wanted to boast about it, and because I was sick. But somebody inside me knew I couldn't, though I wouldn't let him say it.

Nell said: 'You will climb quicker without Johnny in front, and you must adjust your cheese-cutter differently for gliding.'

It became frightfully important to understand this cheese-cutter business, without the extra weight. I was too dithered to work it out in my head.

Everybody looked at me in a covert way.

I was quiet, probably genteel, and certainly very frightened.

Immediately after tea, before I had finished my second cup, Johnny called:

'Come on, Captain.'

I went. It was still complicated and numb. If only one

could explain it. It is probable that my subconscious mind
had got the wind up and decided to stop the solo, not by
saying it wouldn't, but by doing bad landings. I was not
aware of this.

We had to go in ET, which I have never landed. It was
heavy on the stick, light on the rudder. All the springs
(rudder and cheese-cutter) too stiff. I couldn't find the
lovely gliding angle of AV with the cheese-cutter. I
couldn't land at all. Hopeless.

That is the word. There was a constricted feeling of that.

I remember, taxi-ing off, seeing a lark standing about
five feet from the near wing. It didn't fly away. I thought:
'Perhaps this is my last lark.' Also I thought: 'Perhaps I
will be back in time for my second cup of tea, and it will
still be hot.'

Johnny was impatient. After 20 minutes we came in, the
most perilously exquisite vertical sideslip I have been in. I
had been a fool. I had let him down, and myself.

They were still having tea, and said little about it.

Johnny said: 'I am just going to take Mrs. Bernard
home, then I will try you again, when you have had a rest.'

Sitting there, feeling a fool, in a way, but in a way not.

We went again. This time it was JT. Three different
aeroplanes in one afternoon. I think I really did want to do
it this time, even subconsciously, and was cross. But just
as bad.

Johnny side-slipped in again.

Failure.

Such a lot of emotion to get off, and rather tired, so that I
can't put the salt on its tail.

(1) Three separate aeroplanes, bumps, and Johnny's
impatience (he was in a foul temper all day) are a slight
excuse.

(2) I don't want an excuse.

(3) I shall go solo on Friday.

(4) AV's cheese-cutter goes over only ⅛ of its course.
ET's *must* come back, but is too stiff to do so without

forcing. JT's works over about ⅔, but she lacks slots and needs longer holding off.

(5) To-day was 50 min.—20 min.—15 min.
(6) Nell was nice, to comfort me.
(7) Tired out.

14. vi. xxxiv.

Dogs, like very small children, are quite mad. I came in to-night past midnight, after a hospitable evening with a grocer of Shireham (who showed me in his garden a couple of statues that may have been lost, since the second great sale at Park), and I thought I would have a night-cap. It meant opening a new bottle of John Haig. Brown, the Irish Setter who lives with me on the faint supposition that I might be able to train her as a gun dog, was there. I gave her the foil that came off the top of the bottle. It takes half my time to make her eat at all. She cannot be persuaded without the most exhausting efforts to accept anything useful: a bone, a biscuit, anything edible. But the lead foil she accepted as if she were a small boy being given a boat from Basset-Lowke's.

15. vi. xxxiv.

Well, well, well, well, well. Yesterday I had to do some work, so it was impossible. To-day I got over before 10.30, only to find that all the machines were out of action. AV's petrol tank was leaking, ET was not insured, and JT had gone off to Carlands for a top overhaul. It was misty, and Richmond had evidently decided that he would lose his way if he came back. So we hung about the bar, and played with the gambling machines, and generally groused till luncheon.

I am beginning this at the wrong end. On the drive over I tried to reckon out my attitude towards solos. Sub-consciously last time I must have been averse from doing it, and I was certainly terrified. If I had been able to go off in AV I think I should have done it, solely because finding myself alone in the air would have frightened me into my senses. But driving over to-day I was not scared. There was the same intellectual desire to do it, and not the emotional negative. Going solo is rather like committing suicide. One's brain, which must always advocate the suicide's grave as the only reasonable solution, finds itself in conflict with one's vitality. I would recommend a solo flight to all prospective suicides. It tends to make clear the issue of whether one enjoys being alive or not.

Driving over, I knew that I wanted to do it, basically liked being alive; and this time was going to be less scared. I had thought at the end of last time that I should be absolutely unscared. No. I was nervous when I actually thought about it from close to.

I was flagged by a tramp of about 65, and stopped for him. He wanted to go to Middlehampton: said he was glad I had stopped, because he would never have got there: was 'beginning to feel *languid*.' He had walked all night from Warden. It was a warm night, he said, and, proudly, he had not needed to put on his overcoat. He had been flagging people since 8 a.m., but none of them had stopped. I explained apologetically about motor bandits, though anything less like a bandit than this frail, rosy-cheeked old gentleman with his careful overcoat it is difficult to conceive. When I put him down I apologised for lack of money. Oddly enough, it was true that I had not even a penny, as I was in my best suit and had forgotten to change over the cash. He had not asked, and with an unoffended dignity denied a desire for any. He thanked me for what I had done.

Then no machines till luncheon. Then a very good lunch indeed of cold meat, salad, fruit and cream, gorgonzola.

Then Johnny said: 'Off we go.'

It was JT (no slots) and little wind. What there was came

from the east, necessitating a long hold off. We did 30
minutes.

Johnny was in a better temper and I had told him at
lunch that he ought to be more patient with me. The
amazing result of this was that he was. I was landing
badly—bouncing all over the place, swinging my tail, and
not getting to exactly the right mark for my glide in.
Johnny kept having to slip off height for me. Twice, I
think, I had to throttle on and fly round again. But I had
mastered JT's cheese-cutter for the glide. I did one three-
pointer.

Johnny said: 'Two more, and you go.'

The next circuit was passable: a wheel landing, but
effective for its purpose.

The next circuit was a simply terrible bounce.

Johnny said nothing.

I watched the back of his head as we taxied back to the
take off. It looked undecided.

He put her in position and climbed out.

He said: 'Righto. Don't forget she will climb quicker
without me, and glide flatter. For God's sake throttle on
and go round again if you are going to under or overshoot.
You don't need to come down the first time. There's
petrol for half an hour.'

I was not so frightened as before, but still monosyllabic.
I said: 'Yes.'

Johnny said: 'I shall just wait about. Good-bye.'

I said: 'Good-bye.'

Well, I thought, one can begin, at any rate. Life had
become a thing which only existed in fractions of seconds
ahead.

I took off, beautifully it seemed. When I was two feet up
I thought: 'Now it's too late to land.

She climbed buoyantly, feeling much more carefree and
speedy, rising like a balloon.

300 feet. I turned at the road.

I thought: 'Am I frightened?'

Yes.

I thought it would be well to become automatic again, as I had been for the last 30 minutes, instead of going in for feelings.

At the house I turned again, but we were over 400.

I wanted to reach a ride in the northerly wood at 400, bank in along it, switch off diagonally to the field, and come in along the other diagonal, over a red barn.

I was too high, from being alone.

I hurried downstairs: not by switching off and gliding, but by putting the nose down with engine on. This made us go very much faster, which I didn't like. Nor, he said afterwards, did Johnny, a lonely figure in the middle of the aerodrome.

I got the revs exactly where I wanted, but found I was frightened of flying fast.

Then there was a big bump. Do bumps bump more when one is alone? I didn't like it. But one was too busy to feel much about anything.

There was the ride. We spun over sideways, swept along it,* and switched off.

Back came the cheese-cutter. It was a lovely, gentle glide.

I did my gliding turn, beginning to take it off long before it was over. Fine.

To my mild surprise I was pointing exactly for the barn and along my diagonal.

Then I saw that I was going to undershoot. I was going to hit the barn itself with my under-carriage. I kept my hand on the throttle, thinking: 'Give her time, it is not sure, we may just scrape in.' Anyway, it was not much worse hitting a barn than the earth. I felt I could judge it on a foot, and had time to switch on at a tenth of a second. We were going to make it.

*In practically a racing turn, because of the extra speed I had gathered from my descent with engine on. It must have looked very funny from the ground.

We did.

The tail was clear by several feet.

I began to flatten out, to flatten. She was not swinging or yawing and neither of her wings were down. My feet on the rudder bars were perfect.

I was going to come down alive.

We flattened, flattened, straight, perfect, touching, touching, tail, rumble, still straight, even on the ground, and not a bounce. Not a bounce.

He had done his solo.

He shook hands with himself.

He tried to be monosyllabic with Johnny, but was talking fast, because he was still living very fast.

Johnny got on the wing and the step. He taxied him back.

Johnny said: 'I thought you were going to switch on and go round again.'

There were very few people in the club. They came out like disturbed ants.

A girl friend, Ian, Richmond.

They shook hands with Tim—a solemn moment. Then they drank some lager.

In the log-book Solo is written in red ink.

On the way home I wished I had had a little money to give the tramp.

Ker is vanquished.

Chatterly has signalised the occasion by having kittens.

16. vi. xxxiv.

I have few moral feelings about poaching. If a commercial gentleman should turn up and sweep away what has been expensively and often lovingly prepared for sport, solely in order to make a profit by selling the proceeds, then he is a thief and one might disapprove of him, even in the abstract. I have no abstract feelings about the genuine local sportsman-poacher, who does his not very harmful work alone. But I had rather he didn't poach the shoot that belongs to me. If I had the guts, I should go for him in a personal way. Unfortunately I haven't. The only poacher I came across this year was ushered off the premises with two or three nervous sarcasms.

Nobody in the Shire can very well resent the depredations, which are traditional, of Silston and Sisters Singleton. I drive through the former on the way to Credon. The last woodland right was stolen from Silston in 1852, and the theft, and the execution in 1748 of Adams and Tyrell for poaching, has not been forgiven or forgotten. It gives one a vaguely compensatory feeling to know that one has been poached from Silston. The wives of Adams and Tyrell went to the great lord at Park, to beg their husbands' lives. One of them was newly married. The great lord received them kindly, and sent them home with the promise that their husbands should be back in Silston on a certain day. Since he was the landlord whose deer had been poached, and also the magistrate who tried the case (an identification of judge and plaintiff which was common in the 18th century), there was no reason to doubt his word. On the appointed day the husbands came home—but in their coffins.

17. vi. xxxiv.

To-day the ex-observer talked about the war. He was in bombers. Richthofen was sent to deal with their squadron. Once they were shot up from behind and the burst went through the rudder, practically wrecking it, through the end of his nose, and through the propeller. They completed their objective and got back, crashing on the aerodrome. I said: 'Did the C.O. speak to you?' He said: 'Yes, I thought he was mad. But my face was covered with blood and it looked worse than it was. All I knew was that my nose was itching.'

Richthofen's squadron was no particular colour: just a horrible circus of checks, stripes and monsters on the fuselage.

Finally my ex-observer was shot down (through the radiator) in enemy territory. He was taken prisoner in pyjamas.

I said: 'Did you ever shoot anybody down?'

He said: 'Yes, four.'

We were talking about cats falling on their feet. He said: 'I once assisted at rather a disgraceful thing. But it was the sort of thing that happened in the war. We were only 17½, you know. We had an argument about whether chickens could fly, so we took one up and threw it overboard at 500. It did a few stalls and loops for about a hundred feet, then it just shut up and fell like a stone. We felt ashamed of ourselves.'

I said: 'Did you hate the war in the air as much as most people?'

He said: 'No. Generally the better man won, and you had a run for your money, besides having a dry bed and a mess to come back to. But in the next war the aeroplanes will be such lethal weapons, so bristling with machine guns, that the better man won't win. Each machine will bring the other down.'*

Johnny took me at about 3.30. Everybody was groaning about bumps and it was very hot with cumulus clouds and west wind. I flew badly as usual (it was JT) whilst Johnny was in her. After she had been taken away from me, shaken, slapped and given back, I did about half a dozen dud landings. At last Johnny got out. I did a circuit and landed alive, taxied back for him, received a lecture, did another circuit, and landed alive again. There were certainly bumps, but bumps are not specially terrible if you have faith. The wind was gusty and changeable.

*Mouse has since denied this.

Johnny said: 'Righto. Take her up for 20 minutes and do what you like. Keep your eyes open for other aircraft, because there are always a lot about on Sunday. When you come down, do a full circuit of the aerodrome at your landing height, so as to accustom yourself to it.'

Now came the nice part. It was lovely to be free. Against expectation, I am not lonely in an aeroplane. I wheeled and glided over the reservoirs and bathing lakes. Middlehampton was a pool of quicksilver towards the sun. Towns cease to be horrible when you are well above them. The other machines, coming in and going out, hung and crawled with beauty on the earth floor. An aeroplane looks forty times as beautiful from above. For one thing, you get her motion in relation to the earth, and for another you get her colour.

I went up to 1500.

I so wanted to express my freedom and buoyancy. I couldn't loop, daren't spin (partly for fear of Johnny), and didn't even know how to do a vertical bank.

So I dived.

With the engine on. Gingerly. But it was fun. The A.S.I. went 80—90—100—110. At 115 I began to wonder whether one ought to dive with engine on, and whether the wings came off. So we came out. Gingerly also. Then the same again.

I flew to my full limits, exploring all sorts of new and radiant country. Once I lost the aerodrome for a second.

It was time to come down. I shut off and glided, a series of S turns. It was lovely. At 400 I sped round the aerodrome, looking to see if the wind stockings were still the same. They weren't. I had to come in a little to the left.

The turn, the shut–off, the glide, the cheese-cutter, the gliding turn.

We were coming in beautifully.

The earth was near, nearer.

I flattened, flattened, teasing her off the ground.

We stalled at about nine inches, hit a ridge, and, with a little bounce, settled down.

Now I shall never be able to stop flying.

18. vi. xxxiv.

Chatterly's nearly inexhaustible supply of kittens are all black. I thought this seemed odd from a Siamese cat, and rang up her original owner, a doctor with rather cynical views about maternity. I said: 'Look here, about Chatterly. She has had a lot of black kittens. Is that all right?' His merry laugh rattled on the wires. He said: 'Do you know what colour they ought to be?' 'No?' 'Snow white.'

22. vi. xxxiv.

This is the kind of thing that one comes across in the Shire. At Chetood, till the beginning of the nineteenth century, there was a kind of fair called the Chetood Rhyne Toll. It had originally been a right to levy toll on all cattle, sheep, etc., within the bounds of half a dozen parishes. This toll had been levied for a week or a fortnight every year, and it was paid to the baronet of Chetood. His servant had to go forth on the first day of the toll, riding through the villages that bounded the taxable area, blowing a conch shell and distributing cakes with ale to any *boy* who asked for them. There was a tradition, as vague and improbable as the tradition of St. George, that this right had been conferred upon an ancient Chetood, a crusader, because he killed and rid the district of a pestilent boar.

My part of the Shire lay in those days between two great forests, and it was in the southern of these that the boar was reputed to have been slain. The forests were slowly enclosed, and the trees vanished. One day, just beyond Tenmere Wood, a farmer was bringing his last stretch under cultivation. It included a mound grown over with brambles and bracken. He cleared it, and dug it up. Inside were a conch shell, a crusader's sword, and the bones of an enormous boar.

23. vi. xxxiv.

It has blown like fury all the week. On Friday, in a momentary lull, Richmond took AV over to Carlands and was windbound there till to-day. So no flying for me.

To-day Johnny was away with a Credon team to compete in a relay race at a new aerodrome which was opening itself with a kind of gymkhana. Incidentally, our team won it. The result was that only the sergeant-pilot, who is our new second instructor over the weekends, was at Credon to teach me. Named Farrier, he is a quiet fellow of 29, who has done fifteen hundred hours. Exactly the opposite of Johnny, he says that moderate turns are good. I like him much.

The wind was still high and gusty, so I suggested a mild tuition in aerobatics. We did vertical banks, which were grand, and spins. My first purely private spin was amusing, because I understood that the stick had to be centralised (for coming out) rather too firmly. He said: 'Very well, put her into a spin.'

I throttled down, held her up, and, at the moment when she seemed on the point of collapse, gave a good left-footed kick. We dived over our left shoulders, and the ground began its accelerating spin. I was just settling down to view this with pleasure when I was told to come out. I pressed hard on the right rudder, and the roulette board began to come to rest. I pushed the stick too far forward and the aeroplane began to do what I can only conclude would have been an inverted loop.* Farrier grabbed it back on the instant. The next two spins were better, but it is a bore having to come out so soon. I like

*A bunt.

spins, but don't yet feel confident about doing one alone. I must do one more with an instructor, and tell him not to speak.

In vertical banks the controls swop over. You get her nose a fraction below the horizon, give her full throttle gradually, and heel over at the same time. As she passes the normal angle—75°, or whatever it is—you feel the stick wanting to be brought back and top rudder wanting to be applied. I cannot explain this feeling of want. It is not that the controls begin to edge off in those directions: quite the reverse. Only they have to be put thus. Vertical banks are natural. They are instinctive, as I thought flying to be in the earlier stages. The nose keeps on the horizon, but now instead of seeing the line *drawing* across it you see a white strip which fizzes past almost with the speed of a road under a car. My only regret in doing these to-day was that I had to attend to the nose so carefully that I had no time for looking over the edge at the wing standing on end.

I shall practise both these next time I go solo. Or perhaps not the spin.

Now we thought we would do approaches. For a further half-hour (it was a 60-minute lesson) I went round and round like an imbecile, doing a series of hop-skip-and-jump landings which would have sent Johnny into an asylum. Farrier, with tireless good nature, would say, 'That was nearly a good one,' whenever we managed to get down at all. I can't say that I was exactly miserable. I was absolutely dumbfounded, and angry with Farrier for teaching me a new kind of landing (as I thought). We kept coming in apparently far too fast, rushing straight at the earth, and, at the last perilous moment, flattening out into a three-point. Or, rather, this seemed to be so in his demonstrations.

After half an hour of total incompetence I gave her over to him, and he landed me by the sheds. I sat back during this landing and just glanced towards the top wing. This raised the level of my eye at the moment of landing, and did the trick. I shouted the solution to Farrier, the reason why I had been going wrong. As a matter of fact, he had been telling me the same reason once every five minutes himself, but admonition conveys nothing to me. I have to make my own discoveries.

Here was the situation:

(*a*) I had not flown for a week and had partly forgotten where to look while landing.

(*b*) AV has shoulder harness which is tight, and I had to dispense with one of my cushions in order to get into it. So I was sitting low in the seat.

(*c*) Probably the vertical banks and spins had concentrated my attention more directly downwards than it ought to be.

(*d*) The strength of the gusty wind did make it necessary to glide in a little faster. (We seemed to be flattening out at about 65.)

Result of first three clauses: I was looking not half far enough ahead.

Result of last clause: What I was looking down at (instead of along at) seemed to be fairly whistling by.

In fact, what I thought to be a different kind of landing was in reality exactly the same kind, viewed from a new angle. I was looking almost directly down at the daisies. No wonder they rushed at me with such terrifying effect.

I have lost my eye for landings in one week of idleness. I shall have to find out just how much further abroad to look, all over again.

This was a sad instructive lesson, well worth having.

Morals for to-day:

(1) Look ahead.

(2) In gliding turns, *synchronise* rudder and stick.

(3) Hold her down longer in taking off; don't do climbing turns; be more respectful towards my air speed. Farrier remarked on this. He said: 'You will come to a bad end if you continue to fool about with a small margin of velocity.' It is true: not because I am going to stall the

machine as it stands, but because one splutter of the engine will cook me. With 100% efficiency in the engine my behaviour is perfectly safe. In fact, I am flying safely enough, given that what I am flying remains constant. But it might not. So I must do what I'm told; and perhaps I will.

26. vi. xxxiv.

I steamed into the club-room to-day, and one of the young ladies said: 'I hear you smashed up JT on Sunday.' I said: 'Good heavens?' (Awful memories of bumpy landings and thoughts of what might have happened to the under-carriage. It was not till afterwards that I remembered I hadn't flown since Saturday, and then it was AV.)

But she was joking. I said: 'What damage?'

She said: 'Completely written off.'

Then they all began to explain.

JT had been smashed. It happened on Sunday. Poor Farrier, the sergeant pilot, was doing dual with an ex-president of the club: a more than middle-aged man. They did a right-hand circuit for practice, hit the hedge and turned over. No more JT. Neither hurt.

I went to inspect the hedge. There were three or four yards of transverse swath cut out of the next-door cornfield; two fairly tidy gaps in the hedge; a little oil on the aerodrome in two patches; some grass rather trampled and dusty; a few flakes of red paint among the grey blocks, looking bright and sinister like blood from the lungs. It was all that was left of JT. She was a sweet creature, a thoroughbred. She flew to her controls like a miracle, in the kindest way. She was my first solo. Even I could feel that she lived under her stick, going soppy or sweet, but never coarse. She was the apple of Johnny's eye.

The ex-president and the second instructor had left it to each other to switch on. Farrier was too retiring, new and polite, the ex-president too accustomed to Johnny. He expected Farrier to be arrogant and interfere at the least danger. Between them they never throttled on.

The fuselage to the back cockpit was undamaged and they will rebuilt her on that. But she will never be the same. It is a real tragedy.

The wind was gusty from the S.W. and there were threatening showers. Johnny said: 'It is no good for you, Solo.' I said: 'Please, could you teach me something else?' He was not very glad about my having done spins and vertical banks. He said it would make me ham-handed.

When we did go, he had this idea firmly in mind. So I was. We did half an hour of dual circuits, in the course of which I got down safely about three times and superbly once. A real three-pointer. These things are rare enough for record. The other times I was in hot water.

I have not learnt much: in fact nothing new, but I have re-accustomed my eye to looking ahead instead of down. The ground no longer rushes at me.

It was a stormy day.

Once I should have killed myself, if Johnny hadn't been there. A gust took my right wing up on the take-off and I corrected only gently. Johnny gave a strong jerk. At moments like this the quick move is needed. So I have learnt something after all.

The wind fairly took us round on the downwind bank. You could see that we were going crabwise across the ground.

29. vi. xxxiv.

To-day is a happy day. When I got there at about eleven o'clock Johnny was saying good-bye to a fellow in a nice little Comper Swift. Johnny turned round when he was gone and said: 'Good-morning, captain. You will be glad to hear that I wrote off to that newspaper last night, saying you were my best pupil.'

'Thank you very much, my man.' But it was a shatter-ing surprise. I felt a sort of slow pleasure, not at dancing point, like killing a salmon, but a rosy pervasion.

Johnny is in for the King's Cup and wanted to fly round the course. So he pretended that it would be best for me not to do a solo, but to come for cross-country instruction instead. I was far too pleased to feel disappointed, and as a matter of fact it turned out to be a good piece of education.

He showed me how to set the compass, and we set out with two maps.

It is difficult to find one's way in the air. For one thing, main roads look important on the map, and actually less important than the sandy secondary ones when seen from the air. For another, towns confuse you. On the map they are just dots and names. From the air they are intricate heaps of bicycle chain, machine-gun belts, piano key-boards, and motor tyre treads. Lastly, maps are vertical views, but aeroplane views are not. Only the (invisible) point under the aeroplane is vertical.

There was: the Credon reservoir, a superb avenue of trees, a lot of woods, the airship hangars at Cardington (big even from the air, but from the ground evidently immense), trees, folds of country, railway lines (the only lines that live up to the map), an aerodrome, wireless masts, people practising at Hatfield, a railway going into a tunnel, a vast common, acres of glass houses, the superb mowing of a R.A.F. aerodrome (with a beautiful green-red-blue machine taking off below us), a river and a town that ought to have been Hertford but turned out to be Ware. Then there was the nose going down, and the A.S.I. saying 90—100—110. Suddenly there was the tiny yellow pylon in a tiny field surrounded by trees, and almost at the same moment we were standing on our left wing in Johnny's breath-taking vertical turn. I shook my fists above my head, shouting.

There was a time when I got sick of following the map, and watched the wee sheep in the fields, and the crows like little aeroplanes with their shadows, and the country houses with paddocks and practice jumps.

Then another pylon.

We flew the semi-final course and the final.

Finally there was trekking home, not knowing where it was, and taking the stick whilst Johnny did the navigating, and climbing over woody hills, and the same magnificent avenue on the right this time, and the infinitely distant murky dot of the aerodrome, and Johnny making something which ought to have been (but wasn't) a bad landing, and swearing at the air.

We must have been away an hour and a quarter.

At luncheon Horsey turned up, the soloist before me, and went up with Johnny for a few circuits, and did three moderate landings of his own.

Later on, Johnny took me. We did two or three circuits, with moderate landings, and Johnny got out. He said: 'Go on and do twenty minutes or so yourself. Don't forget that it's very gusty. If things aren't going well, go round again. Don't practise landing. Do turns; and remember the boy scout: let every turn be a good one.'

I felt a little frightened. It was the result of this foul-weather break. However, I said good-bye and went off. The take-off was good. One had to be absolutely into wind (strongish, gusty and from N.W.). It was bumpy as well as gusty.

At 2000 I began to feel cold as well as frail. I wandered aimlessly round, wondering where to practise S-turns. On the south side of the aerodrome I should be interfering with possible arrivals (and might be run into, which was more important.) On the north side there was a very bumpy wood. On the other side I should be S-turning across wind and was too inexperienced to know whether this would be a good thing or not. I compromised by doing two lots, south and north. In neither case did I feel very happy with them (AV is so pitifully soggy compared with JT) and particularly not on the north. Somehow I feared to develop into a spin.

I gave it up and decided to practise approaches. I did one from 2000 (overshoot), one from 1000 (perfect), and about four from anything between 400 and 1000. All except the first would have done. But I had been told not to practise landings, so I throttled on at 20 ft. each time, and went round again.

My watch said: Go home.

I did a complete circuit at 400, fussing very particularly about revs and altitude and points to fly to. Cut off. Glided. Held her into wind. Kept the gliding speed at about 64. Flattened out. A three-pointer.

30. vi. xxxiv.

These innumerable Credon circuits, pounding tipsily along from landmark to landmark, seem to bear little relation to the ground. And yet it is there, a rich red loam suitable for turnips. The droning circles receive attention from the ground, I suppose. The villages must be aware of them, Understone, Poulton, Halfcote, Myers, Thornby and Picton. Yet the villages are as strange to me in the air, indeed stranger, than the people of distant ages. Credon belonged to the Count of Mortain under Doomsday, later to the monks of Middlehampton and the nuns of Aunestowe. At Understone, which is famous for its ash trees (a tree is odd from the air, with its top leaves the intimate ones) there used to be a tree called The Golden Ash. It had steps up it. And it was here also that Sir Walter Manny lived, if he ever came home. I know more about him than I do about the present owner, because Froissart's Chronicles were among my early loves. It is odd to think that this toy, tin-pot, inverted house, wheeling under an anxious eye, belonged to that great warrior. It makes a short-circuit to my childhood. I can remember reading

about him by a red brick wall, on a green lawn, in sunlight.
So this is where he came from. Fortunately he lived up to
the traditions of the Shire, went elsewhere to fight his
battles. He was buried elsewhere, also: so he at least, of all
the inhabitants of six sleeping villages, will not be worried
by my persistent drone.

1. vii. xxxiv.

The air pageant of yesterday seems tied up with to-day's
flying, in its muddled way. For it gave me the spectacle of
my first crash actually happening, and fatal. The left-hand
man of a Hawker Hart squadron★ lost his engine as he was
leaving the aerodrome, after the salute. He couldn't go on,
because of the houses. He must have had 600 ft. and at least
130 m.p.h. in hand. He banked in sharply to the left,
looking absolutely panic stricken, did not give himself
enough room to turn into wind, as he wanted to do; got
the idea that he was going to stall; tried to land cross-wind;
found himself too near to the ground; didn't flatten out in
time. He seemed to make a very fast, crabwise wheel and
wing-tip landing. His fuselage turned over sideways
inside the wings. The wings sat down floppily from on
top. There was practically no noise. About the same as a
rowdy tail skid on a very dry ridge at Credon. The
machine was first a thing that was free to fly and wheel;
then it was a weak thing that had flopped like a shot heron.
The wings seemed flexible in the way they curled over:
much more like dough or something, than wood and
fabric. The army of mechanics were rushing out from the
covey of aeroplanes on the right. I said, more to show off
than with sincerity: 'Thank God he hasn't caught light.'

When the little men were only a score of yards away
(and why did they seem to get there before the ambulance

★The following account is only the opinion of an inexperienced
spectator. I am sorry if the emotions seem heartless, but I thought telling
the truth might make up for that.

cars and engines?) there was a little red lick of oil flame. Then black smoke. Not columns of it, not a raging inferno (for it was in strong sunlight) but just the lazy red fire and curling smoke.

The observer had got clear somehow. The pilot was burned.

There are morals and feelings attached to this. The pilot ought to have taken a much wider gliding turn, or, alternatively, landed down wind. He had plenty of room to do this, and the wind was negligible. Also I believe R.A.F. shock absorbers had something to do with it. Nearly all the landings done that afternoon looked from a distance like wheel landings. I believe★ R.A.F. pilots get into this habit because they have such magnificent absorbers (and perhaps well-mown and rolled aerodromes?). Anyway, they put their machines down fast on their wheels, run along, and lower their tails. Just like me. This is faintly *à propos* of a wheel and wing tip crash, though of course the man did it at high speed and with the appearance of being panic stricken.

What did people feel about this, and what did I? First, I was excited and glad. I don't think I was singular. Peter's education made him speak about the 'poor fellow,' but when a flying boat looked like crashing a little later on he was the first to climb on the top rail to see every bit of it. It was a thrill. Curiously indefinable. Later on, when the next event was doing something daring, the dead man became more real. He had been daring, too. So one felt a small twinge of remorse for him, nothing else. One did not feel sick or frightened (it is I!) as one does with motor smashes by the side of the road. One was much more remote.

All this has a bearing on to-day's efforts. I turned up early and Johnny took me in AV at about 11.30. He said: 'You're heavy to-day. What were you doing last night? Rolling in the hay?'

★April xxxv. Not now.

We did an overshoot and two dud landings. Johnny got out. He said good-bye and hit me on the back of the neck. (Here comes a chopper to chop off your head. Chop-chop-chop.) I went away, as usual flying better since now responsible. I was to do landings at ten-minute stretches.

Johnny had been rude about my gliding speed. I was tending, as usual, to drop below 60 as I came in. He, no doubt exaggerating, told me I should kill myself quite soon. Now, at 2000 ft., I was doing gliding turns without confidence. I was hammy and hazardous. The first landing was good, particularly as there was practically no wind and a patient hold-off necessary.

I went again, half heartedly practised those accursed S-glides (never feeling trustful of the cheese-cutter) and came in a little after time. I flattened out too high and landed with a bounce.

Well, I couldn't stop on that. Whether I had been told not to practise landings or not, I had to end with a decent one. I went round again and dropped from feet. I didn't know whether to throttle on or not, so I gave her a burst. The next bounce was as high. About five more bounces, whilst I made up my mind not to throttle, and we were down, feeling shaken and ashamed. I taxied back to the sheds, feeling afraid, and not knowing whether I should get into trouble if I did another. Johnny hadn't seen, but I told him. I had done right to stop.

After lunch we went again. Again I was a lump. We tried the new machine that had been sent to replace JT. WN I think it was. The rudder was stiff in its fuselage slots. So we went back to AV. (WN is sweeter, almost as nice as JT.) Johnny got out after two circuits, and off I went. This was a curious show. I must have done more than half a dozen circuits for each landing. I simply couldn't put her down. First it would be undershot, then overshot, then flatten out too high, then bounce on the wheels. I began to feel I never should get her down. It became tiresome more than anything else: not frightening, though

I asked myself at the time, to see if it was. At last I got her down—a good landing. We went off again at once; and exactly the same thing happened. Round and round, feeling exasperated and suspended inside. At last it looked like a possible and I went for it. We came down on one wheel, and that on the fatal ridge. The whole machine leaped into the air and began to slew towards the left. I kicked violently on the right rudder, and no response. The right wing was sweeping within inches of the baked grass. The aileron did nothing to raise it up. I used the other rudder, and then both, one after the other, in a panic. All the time there were a lot of wings pointing at unaccustomed angles and a lot of bumps. We were down and still slewing. By the grace of God alone the angles cleared themselves up, and nothing touched. We were at right angles to our line of approach: a really spectacular landing. I taxied back, trying to pretend that this was just rather a quick taxi-ing turn, and started off again. Honour demanded it. I couldn't fly any better. The first circuit I flattened too high and went round again. All the time the cheese-cutter and this cursed 64 on the A.S.I. was bothering me at the come in. (Perhaps I ought to come in from higher and further, thus giving myself more time to settle down on the glide.) The next time I got cross and determined to land whatever the consequences. It was a wheel landing and a bounce, but not terrible. I taxied in, and began to grin. There was a good crowd at the aerodrome and most of the time they had stood in rows on the roof, watching me like Peter and the flying-boat. Or like Chatterly watching a sparrow. I found myself grinning more and more. I had made their flesh creep.

After tea Johnny said: 'You've done your three hours. Now we'll do your height test.' He began to fuss with the barograph. I found that I was feeling nervous, incapable and tired. There was a man doing stunts in WN and I was terrified that he would run into me.

I went up to 3,000. Johnny's spirit told me where to shut

off, and we began the interminable series of figure-eight turns.

The ghost told me what to do all the time, and very sadly I did it. I was absolutely whacked. Now there was time for just one more. Now I was to try and do a decent landing. Now I had hit with my wheels. Now I was putting on engine and something was taking it off. 'No,' said the ghost, 'you are quite right, but it would have spoilt the barograph.' We bounced and were still.

At last there was looking at the wet mauve ink on a perfect chart, feeling empty, and signing a lot of papers with a shaken signature, and driving home, after a kind of oral examination, and feeling almost too sick to eat my dinner.

This was after the pageant.

2. vii. xxxiv.

I suffer from unaccountable lapses of sympathy, not entirely based upon the propinquity of the object. I cannot pretend to have been sorry for the man at the display. At a clay-pigeon shoot for the Warden farmers, where I was scoring, one of the farmers had a gun with a defective nipple. When he shut the gun it went off. As the scorer, whose business it was to record every kill or miss, I had completely fallen into the rhythm of pull—whizz— bang—tick, and this bang, unpreceded by any pull or whizz, immediately attracted my attention. My table was commandingly placed behind the shooting mark and I saw the whole play. The gun was pointing at an angle of 45 degrees to the trap, and there was a tree about forty yards away in this direction. It remained a vague tree, whilst you could count four, and then it began to spawn boys. They rose up from its roots and trekked away, relinquishing the fatal spot with every appearance of revulsion. Their minds seemed to make no connection with the shooting point, or even the pigeon trap. It was the tree from which they fled

with loathing. Two of the boys began to stagger, one of
them doubling up and the other bleeding from above and
below the eye. It was the first time I had seen two boys out
of one covey, with a single barrel, and my exclamations of
dismay were purely formal. I am sorry to say that neither
of them was seriously injured.

3. vii. xxxiv.

I was thinking to-day what a lot of things there are
which ought to be written about, and don't get it. One
says to oneself at the time: 'I must enter that up.' And then
something intervenes: one forgets: there is such a lot to do,
that one can't find time merely to write. I can think of two
such things in the past month. I watched a kingfisher
fishing within half a dozen paces; and caught an elephant
hawk moth, the lesser variety.

The kingfisher was on a Sunday morning. I had slept in
the open beside the lake overnight, watching the con-
stellations close above my face, pretending that I could
suddenly leave the surface of the earth and fall up towards
them. I singled out the star which was nearest to being
vertically above my erected nose, because that would
obviously be the one towards which I should fall, before I
drifted to sleep. I woke before dawn. It doesn't seem to
come at any particular time on a hot summer day. I woke
in time to hear the birds starting, cuckoo first, then blackbird, robin, thrush.

I was there because I wanted to fish for tench, who stop
taking soon after breakfast. Float fishing is a job which I
don't personally care for, but a four-pound tench on a
trout rod makes it worth trying occasionally. And it was
not unpleasant sitting in a world that largely slept, in the
summer mist which ushered in a baking day after a warm
night, visited by natural companions at rare intervals: a
pair of mallard, a carrion crow floating off to his inimical
rounds, a grey squirrel. Solitary visitors, they served to

emphasise the solitude, and shewed little distrust of a rather blear-eyed, unshaven, early angler. Fishermen are accepted without fear by most birds and beasts. We have a name for meekness and standing still.

But tench want an off-shore wind, and none came. I gave in and bathed in the silent water, then set off home at about eleven o'clock, along deserted paths. In the green alley between the two lakes I was startled by a big splash, out of sight. It was as noisy as a large trout leaping clean out, and I thought it was a fish. The small perch and roach jump out of the water when the pike are feeding, but the loudness of the wallop made me want to see this one, and I pushed through the bushes to get a view. It was as loud a slap as a big tench would make, wallowing. Just as I got to view, the leap happened again: but instead of the thing falling back into the water after the commotion, it rose out of it. It rose, and darted slewing round a bush, with that unmistakable electric flash that is a kingfisher.

It was a glow of pleasure: just as the elephant hawk moth was, which I caught in my top-hat, standing on a table, at two in the morning; and gave away next day to a collector with pardonable pride.

4. vii. xxxiv.

First landing off an aerodrome. To-day a couple of young men turned up in a Gipsy I and landed in one of our own highly unsuitable fields. I was introduced to the pilot at tea, made friends with him. He suggested that he could have taken me to Credon if I wanted to fly there, but the trouble was how to get me back, as he was in a hurry. I said: 'Well, take me there for a drink and bring me back at once.'

He was a grand person called Vell. He took off across the valley, with the smallest possible run, banked to the left to avoid the obelisk, and to the right to lift his wing over the trees. It was faintly exciting, in an interested way, wondering what sort of a pilot he was and how efficient. He was nothing like so firm as Johnny, but fairly assuring. There was nothing in the front cockpit except an A.S.I. which had an error of 10 m.p.h., and no stick.

We flew to Middlehampton more or less by guess and thence to Credon by eye. It was a hot and lovely day, with haze all round the horizon, but clean bright fields below. It was nice to watch things underneath without having to worry: the fields mown round the edges with mathematical exactitude, so that the different colours of corn made them look like blank framed pictures; abandoned goal-posts lying flat for the summer, with our shadow scooting over them; Middlehampton looking reddish and vast, so that one wondered 'What about an engine failure?' At the same moment Vell began to climb, with my faulty A.S.I. horrifyingly saying 45.

At Credon we landed with a side slip, very fast, touched with a slightly bouncy wheel landing, stopped just before the little flags on the fatal ridge.

We left again, taking off down wind. There was hardly any.

Landing in the home field was a kick. We circled over the trees, cut off, side-slipped off height (too much), just scraped in over Farmer Williams' wire fence, found the opposite side of the valley zooming at us, pointed our nose in the air, and banged into the steep uphill with a bounce, hardly running ten yards. It made one think.

5. vii. xxxiv.

First of all it was as hot as hell, and the wind was different in every stocking. AV was having a top overhaul, so it had to be WN, whose rudder bar is stiff. We took off with a waggle and Johnny forcibly continued it for about twenty violent wags the moment we were off the ground, out of bad temper. It was like being shaken for being naughty. Then a dud landing because Johnny was insisting on my landing cross-wind and because the pitot tube had packed up. Only the tin indicator was working and that sluggishly. As I lack any instinct for my gliding speed this was disconcerting. After another dud landing we blew through the pitot tube (a bad thing, according to my flying book) and it decided to work. Then I complained about being made to land cross-wind and we decided on another direction. The wind altered again the moment we were in the air, and blew from a fresh quarter altogether. Result, another cross-wind landing with Johnny holding the windward wing down, stick to wind. We decided to stop till things had settled down.

Half an hour later we tried again. Still variable gusts, but at least two of the three stockings said the same. After a dud landing Johnny climbed out. Again I was not to practise landings: in fact, I was forbidden to land except at the end of my trip. I cleared off, did half a dozen approaches (mildly shooting up the aerodrome at the end of each), two vertical banks (losing 100 feet in each), and a few gliding turns from 2,000. Went to look at the reservoir. It was a very bumpy day. Then I came in for tea, making a six-foot bounce and neglecting to put my tail down in the midst of it. Lesson number one for to-day: if the bounce is not terrible, hold the tail down and let it rip. But hold the tail down. Very important lesson.

At tea Johnny spilled his cup over his trousers and said: 'Down my legs again. What a naughty girl I am!'

After tea I asked for another go, and said: 'Don't worry if it's a nuisance.' I meant by this: 'Don't come for preliminary circuits, because I think I can do it alone.' I didn't like to say this actually. Johnny said: 'No, no. I'll come and see you off.'

I thought: 'He means to do a circuit dual, to make sure.' But when I got in, it transpired that I was going to be trusted after all. I was to be allowed to take-off by myself, for the first time, without preliminary. It didn't matter that I had had some dual an hour or two before. It was an advance. Johnny gave me a little lecture and we were off.

I did approaches and one protracted vertical turn at 2,000. That is what it began at. After about two and a half circles we were at 1,800. Perhaps that is an exaggeration. Anyway it was perfectly safe and great fun. There was not much horizon to help: only silver haze and the great ball of the sun. Then I produced my afternoon's achievement. I went back to 2,000, shut off, and glided in with figures of eight. They were absolutely perfect. I came into the aerodrome about ten feet above the hedge and throttled on again when my wheels were almost touching. This was because I had been told not to land except at the end of my performance, and had ten minutes in hand. But it was a moral victory. Even if my barograph for the A licence was a fluke, at least I now feel that I can do one to order—with luck. Good. After more practice approaches I came in with something like a three-pointer, taxied to the sheds, and went home in a medium glow.

6. vii. xxxiv.

WN again. To-day was so much like yesterday that it deserves little. One or two small things, however. For instance, it was the first time that Johnny let me go off solo the moment I arrived, without any dual at all. I was still not to practise landings. It was bumpy, blazing and the ground like iron. Nor is our aerodrome very flat. I soberly went off and did half a dozen figures of eight round two close marks (one at each end of a field, a farm building and a tree) at 600 feet precisely. This was a repetition of a test for an A licence. There was no barograph this time, but I kept my eye on the altimeter and that stayed at 600 all the time, as near as no matter. Then I went up to 2,000 and did another glide in figures of eight, coming in perfectly, so that it was agony to switch on and go round again. Then a few more approaches from different altitudes: mostly undershoots. I am apt to forget that the right-angled approach loses height on both arms of the angle.

For instance, one can come in from the same altitude in any of the following ways:

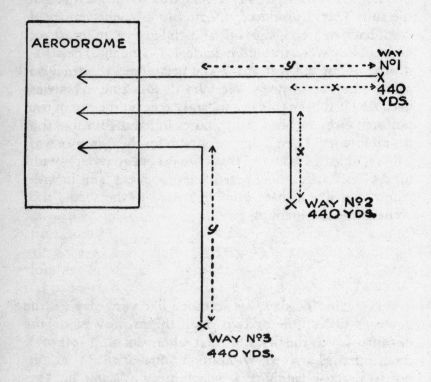

Switch off in each case at the cross. In the first case I have switched off on a line quarter of a mile away. In the second only one-sixth of a mile. In the third only one-twelfth of a mile. But in each case I have glided the full quarter. (This, of course, is only theoretical: because it does not allow for wind.)

At the end of my morning's flight I took two shots to land. The first was far too close to the hedge. (I ought to have gone round again.) Instead, I crawled in, lost a great deal too much forward ↓ speed, ↘ and *dropped* on my wheels more like this ↓ than this ↘ . Throttled on and went round again, landing this time with a definite, though single, bounce.

At lunch Johnny said that I was getting idle. I was to stop doing climbing turns and throwing the machine about. It was better flying to be gradual and gentle. He was displeased. So after lunch he would take me dual.

When after luncheon came, the wind, like yesterday's at the same hour, had gone crazy. It blew from everywhere between E.N.E. and S.E., at ten-second intervals and differently in all parts of the aerodrome. Three or four landings with drift, packets of oaths, and we gave in. Sad.

8. vii. xxxiv.

Again Johnny sent me off without dual and, as last Sunday, I performed miserably. After the gliding turns and approach circuits which seem to be becoming my staple food, I did a leap-landing which only just fell short of the right-angled skid that brought the house down last week-end. It was a terrible business, complicated by the fall-away of the contours towards the N.E. of the aerodrome. On these occasions it is God who protects my undercarriage.

I took off again, against orders, to do it properly. This time it was a single bounce, ending with the tail nicely down, and not very foul. As a matter of fact, it was *nearly* a worse one than ever, for I began to slew with a gust or something at the last moment, and had to jab like hell with my right foot. The moral becomes more and more apparent that at critical moments near the ground, when the flying speed is unhappy, a sharp movement of the controls is quickly necessary.

Taxied in, with my tail between my legs.

The scenario writer went solo yesterday and is very

happy. He reports Johnny as saying: 'If you undershoot
and try to hold her nose up on the gliding turns, so as to
scrape in, you stall, and then, before you know where you
are, we're all walking along behind you with our heads
bowed and our hands behind our backs.'

Johnny's King's Cup machine appeared to-day. A Miles
Hawk with, I think, Gipsy III engine, handicapped to do
142 m.p.h. It is the sweetest-looking aeroplane: spats,
streamlines, everything ivory white. Johnny is not pleased
with the handicap.

It was a good day really: air-minded till lunch, county-
minded at a tennis party till supper, and beer-minded,
playing nap at Tenmere, till they closed.

13. vii. xxxiv.

The Shire still possesses some of its oldest families. The
best of them has continuously occupied the same house for
five hundred years. I should like to see the inside of such a
place. It seems that the lived-in-ness of the antiquity gives
it a startling reality, a feeling of time telescoped and
eternity. I dare say you would find a pair of crusader's
boots under your bed, owing to the boot-boy having
muddled them, and probably there are a couple of battle
axes or rapiers mixed up with the umbrellas in the hall.

This family, from living so long in the Shire, has come
to be typical of it in every way. For instance, they are still
commoners: a peerage or a baronetcy would have been a
bit extreme. Only one of them ever troubled to appear in
history. He went up to London as a Member of Parli-
ament. However, after his single and maiden speech,
which was directed against the Scots, King James bundled
him straight back to the Shire. I like to think of the family
mouth opening just once, in all those years, and being so
instantly silenced.

14. vii. xxxiv.

Johnny 2nd in King's Cup.

21 and 22. vii. xxxiv.

I left the home field with Roland Vell at noon on Saturday. After Heston for customs, we flew to Le Zoute; Heston; an aerodrome in Wiltshire. One Sunday, home for a job of work; Credon for lunch; Lympne for tea, landing at a busman's aerodrome for petrol on the way; Heston for dinner. But we got into a bar instead. After that we flew to a marriage party at the Hoo. Finally home.

Roland was the pilot. As I had nothing to do in the front cockpit, I scribbled all Saturday:

'Traffic at Heston. Ford Below. Cemetery tooth-pick spillikins. Keyboard treads. Toy grey flat glass river wash slow nosing motionless Bassett Lowke. More Gothic piqué regularity of London armadillo or horned toad. Vibro massage. Cut out? The Oval proud to recognise. Probably not. Was. Australians? Roland: "I wonder what the press would say if we shot them up?" White dentelles of Tower Bridge. Timber boats at docksides yellow just like river wrack. Bunkers golf smallpox. White beards of barges. 4-5,000. Forbidden area. Ammunition dump? Real liners? Suddenly cloud white rushing at whisps blank thin out more coming kick enjoy fear? Valkyre charge. Under us. Frightening that it should go so fast. Down at 120. Want to smoke. Chalk. Amusing fort near Rochester Aerodrome. Stooked corn like pin-stripe trousers. Clouds again black above. Air line crossing thick mist. Nice little engine scooting along by itself looking busy. The scrofulas of the earth. Sick? Lympne. The grey mud sealine ending the world. Mist. Out of the world through the back cloth. Clouded linoleum. One seagull. A flake. Capri. Sweet saliva in mouth. Ships. Tankers. Mother hippo. Practically no bumps over sea (all near Lympne) flat as hat. Clearer. Little cloud? Streak? *France*. The small oblong numerous serf-fields of N. France and Belgium. Patch quilt or parquet? Inlay. Zeebrugge indistinct interest. Coming back sand racing. The cross on the hill near air route (Ashford?) 8,000 feet over Wiltshire the great saffron cloud towers. Lux. Soapsuds. Sun starboard. Moon port. Earth blue. This keen air. Going at them. The feeling of don't dare to stunt or flying anything but straight and level at this insignificance. Be careful. Be modest. Beware. Distrust of wings and tail. Going at. I shake with cold and fear. But going through I like? Till he curls. Then cling in terror.'

On Sunday I didn't write anything, because I had the maps and was navigating. We had a rainstorm crossing the air route this time. Blind. Thunderstorm at Lympne. Flew to the marriage feast in formation with a Gipsy I, driven by a mad B licence pilot. Hands off. Petrol off. Pick nose. Point at aerodrome. Absurd. Shoot up in Prince of Wales. Frightful field to land in. Nearly spun in shooting up afterwards. Roland most dashing and skilled. But confident. He will wipe himself off. Give him two years.

Lots to drink.* Now I could find my way anywhere, I think. How far and fast!

23. vii. xxxiv.

The salmon, and the fact that my trouting rod has been stolen, and the frenzy for aeroplanes, have put me off trout fishing for the time being. It is the old story of never having enough time for what one wants to do. Flying over Wiltshire yesterday, we followed the course of a little river. Hanging over Cobbett's favourite country, with the sharp downs to provide a skyline of *useful* beauty, and the fertile valleys full of comfort and richness between them, it was almost an agony of affection to look down into the

---

*As this seems to be the only excuse, in Civil aviation, for flying from one place to another: a thing everybody wants to do.

clean water. You could see the whole geography of the stream, the bright green cresses, almost the shadowy trout with their undershadows.

Nothing will beat the dry-fly. One may have momentary crazes, stunning super-pleasures like the buoying aeroplane and the freezing spring salmon, but ultimately one will come back. For the dry-fly is the highest of the arts. You have got to endure for a salmon, and there is a pleasure in the absolutely straight sizzle of gut culminating in the plop of a lure that will be fishing efficiently through the whole arc, and the ten minutes with the fish on are at the tip of life. But you can't stalk a salmon. You don't caress your cast on to the water with a feathery anxiety.

There is something in our effete old English waters after all. Though they don't go red and quick and talkative, the sun dances on their ripple. The birds sing beside them in the crystal light, the artificial may-fly goes zzt-zzt in the air above them. And in them stands absorbed the ruminant angler, unconscious of time, deft with his fingers, puzzling his beloved fly-box, breathing his pipe smoke regularly in the bliss of concentration, pitting his quivering wits and tackle against the rosy-spotted tiger-fighters of the drinkable water, sun-struck into another infinite universe like the heron. I suppose the heron must be the happiest of living creatures.

25. vii. xxxiv.

Half an hour solo. It was bumpy, with a strong wind, so that it was impossible to overshoot. I flew well.

One of the things that get a new slant from the air is the agriculture of the Shire. It seems sometimes from the land, one has to admit, a bit woolly and haphazard. From the air it is incredibly neat. I should like to fly one of these urban know-alls, who laughs at Farmer Garge, over the country. I should like to ask him whether he could lay out this geometrically perfect rectangle of hedgerows, on land which is all uphill and down-dale from the human level, without the aid of a surveyor. Yet our fathers did it.

26. vii. xxxiv.

It was inadequate to say on the 14th that Johnny was second in the King's Cup. It makes nothing of the story of the earlier stages (which I may have wrong, for I only know them by report) in which Johnny's heat was flown in a thunderstorm, the sky black, the aerodrome lost in the upleap of rain, the spectators under the hangars so that everything seemed deserted; and how one by one the machines gave up, being reported down here and there at a few minutes interval over the loudspeakers; and how nothing was heard of Johnny, until he was the only one unaccounted, half an hour overdue. It makes nothing of the feeling for him that was almost palpable over the aerodrome, and the affection, nearly obituary, in the loud-speaker's confidential voice. Nor does it, nor could I, give a picture of the black sky out of which a tiny aeroplane draggled itself, lonely and exhausted. It was something about human splendour.

There was the final round, and the agony of seeing Johnny handicapped by something like a quarter of an hour, so that the first machines had completed their circuit before he left the ground. There was the rapture of watching him catch up, bearing up on them, hauling them down, and nailing them dead, one after another. There was his exquisite white low-winged monoplane suddenly perpendicular to the earth as he swept round the pylon. Nothing spectacular, he flew at a constant minimum height, flat-out, with effortless smoothness. Then there was a black hatred of the Monospar, whose handicap made it impossible for him to win, and the wretched thing arriving minutes ahead of everybody else, and the rest coming in within seconds of each other, after Johnny had sternly flown his way to their best place on a beautifully adjusted handicap.

It was upon a holiday
When shepherds, grooms, have leave to play,
I cast to go a-shooting!

Long wandering up and down the land,
With bow and bolts in either hand,
For birds in bushes tooting.

COLIN CLOUT

19. viii. xxxiv.

The high hats look amazed when I tell them that I live in a country pub, and the High Brows look contemptuous. I have difficulty in explaining to the former that no, 'pub' is not my playful way of describing one of the very comfortable hotels in Ferneley (as opposed to the simple comforts of Claridges): and it is quite impossible to explain to the latter that I live in the country because I prefer it, and not because I want to be Rousseau. Intrinsically there are few reasons why one shouldn't live in a pub and shave in the kitchen: if one can afford to. It is a simplification of life, which leaves room for other things. I have forgotten who the philosopher was who went to live in a cabin in order to make things easier. He bought one beautiful vase for the delight of his eye, and sat down to contemplate it. After some days he noticed that its inexhaustible pattern was obscured by dust. He dusted it patiently; but two days later it was just as bad. He threw it out of the window. My pub throws a lot of nonsense out of the window. Besides, they are lovely people.

It is nice to go in fear of my life with my hostess, and to eat what she gives me when she chooses to give it, and to pay close attention when she speaks (instead of wool gathering), and to mind my p's and q's. Freedom lies in the recognition of necessity. It took a long time to kiss the rod: but now I am free to do as I'm told. It is a benevolent despotism, not unkind and not really unbending. Mrs. Warm is a sultana because her will is stronger than mine, not through brutality. We understand each other after a series of bitter quarrels. We are the same family.

It is nice to sit arguing with Jimmy, her consort, in the tap-room after the customers have been turned out: to watch the firelight on his red hair, and to sup up his friendly liquor in the long winter nights that are coming, knowing that there is a roof over our heads in the bitterest weather, whatever may be the lot of other poor devils lost in the dark.

And the best is to be trusted to run the pub for a week at a time, when he goes away for his summer holiday: and to wash the glasses, and tap the barrels, and serve, and sleep alone with the till by the bedside: and to shew good takings when he comes back from the Yorkshire moors.

As a professional barman, I believe I might have been able to make good.

21. viii. xxxiv.

Jimmy Warm woke me at 4.30. Puffy and unshaven, we drank rum and coffee by electric light. It was getting light at 5.15, and Sergeant Allweather had not arrived. Jim only had a stupid .22 rabbit-rifle affair. He went round the bottom of the Eleven Acre, to try and put the duck out of the reeds, and I went up to my old stand on the octagon, where it narrows. Brown went with me. Nothing came from Jim's end. I waited, looking both ways. In quarter of an hour they came, a stately flight of about four, from the Roof House End. I missed both barrels. Jimmy turned them, or else it was another lot. They were mallard, but it was still very dim. I think I had two more misses. Then I killed one. He went into the water-lilies with a swash, stone dead. A flight of five caught me unawares, almost settling whilst I was loading. I missed these, with both barrels. They settled on the opposite side, in the reeds. It is lovely to see ducks settle. They turn into wind perfectly, like a squadron of aeroplanes, and glide, and hold off stick, and back-pedal at the last moment, and stall, and begin to preen themselves, shaking their wings into place at once.

Allweather arrived, and I made him take the first shot at them. He missed. I missed from the opposite bank. The sergeant and I were now on either side of Octagon and the birds were coming well. I killed another, but it didn't seem a clean kill. He fell just outside the water-lilies. By now it was bright day. Allweather and Jimmy went down to the Eleven Acre whilst I took the punt to retrieve my birds, with only two cartridges left. Five came over whilst I was paddling about. I got one hard so that he fell out of the flight, landed on the Eleven Acre and couldn't get up. Allweather killed another. But this part I only heard about later. I searched the water-lilies for more than an hour, but couldn't find my clean kill. Either he was under the leaves or a pike had taken him, or he may have been a Tufted and held on to the bottom. But I'm sure it wasn't the latter because he came down so beautifully, in somersaults, probably shot through the head. Anyway I couldn't find him. The other was quite dead and outside the lilies. At about eight o'clock I gave up looking. There were a lot of feathers behind the second island, where another bird that I thought I might have touched came down under control.

When I got round to the Eleven Acre I saw the sergeant and Jimmy walking along under a canoe. I went to them and said brightly. 'Well, had any luck?' Allweather said indignantly: 'We've had a something ducking!' They were both covered with black mud to the armpits. So was Brown. They had taken the canoe to retrieve the two duck mentioned before, and Brown had got excited and upset it. The funny thing was that, having already soaked themselves to the skin, they took the canoe ashore and *carried* it home. They didn't get the duck. Standing in three feet of black mud, on either side of the canoe, they had reflected about duck shooting. 'If this,' said the sergeant, 'is what he wants his fifty cartridges for, he can put them where the monkey keeps his nuts.' I took their photographs as a memento.

22. viii. xxxiv.

We got up at 4.30 again to-day, but there was nothing much doing. Three came over at 5.25, which I missed with one barrel: two at 5.45, which I left to Jim. Seven came at 6.15, which again I missed with one barrel, more in the hopes of turning them than anything else. At 6.45 one more came over and him I spared with both barrels. They were all long shots, not worth taking except for the excitement of being early in the season. Jim only fired once. I kept leaving them to him and shouting 'Over.' But nothing happened. He had borrowed a gun from the policeman. It was a good gun, except that it had never been cleaned and the last cartridge (discharged) had been left in it. The discharged cartridge had rusted in. So it always jammed just before Jim wanted to fire.

The bats were still flying in the early dim. A big dragon-fly rattled its wings on the reeds. The big ones curl their bodies up, the blue ones down. The duck came over, so unbirdlike: smooth, purposeful, apparently slow—the snake neck stretched out with the little knout at the end of it, sighted on a certainty. The last duck circled us, very high, with the bright dawn tinting his breasting feathers, so that he looked like a pochard, and the wee viper-knot of his head turning this way and that, directly above us, with anxious curiosity.

Two Shireham anglers were fishing the Eleven Acre. They had two tench on gentle and lob worm. The larger looked about 3 lbs. I watched the second being taken. It all seemed a bit lethargic. But I liked their red eyes, tunny-coloured bodies and viscous fins.

I went again in the evening at 7.20, and waited till about 9 o'clock (sunset approximately 8.20?) but nothing came; except a solitary duck, who was high and out of range on the far side of the lake. First it was a fine evening, with the swallows high and cirro-cumulus clouds, so that I thought it would be a fine day to-morrow. But the clouds got ragged, the gnats were blown away (I smoked cigarettes till my tongue was sore), the swallows went to bed, and even the dozens of bats got less enthusiastic. The rain came.

I was alone, and had stepped in the water with my Sunday shoes. It got darker and darker. When I couldn't see the bats at five paces I came home, deciding to give the duck a week's rest.

23. viii. xxxiv.

Clouds are an interesting hobby, not only for the aeronaut, but for anybody who lives in the country; because they have a direct bearing upon the weather, like the wind. It appears that there are about four main kinds of cloud, which couple with one another and breed offspring, each having a special relation to the kind of day. The four main kinds are Cirrus, Cumulus, Stratus and Nimbus.

The Cirrus cloud, who lives at very high altitudes, in the neighbourhood of thirty thousand feet, can perhaps best be represented like this:

He is a *fibrous* cloud, a whispy stationary sort of mare's tail: a bending, diverging or exploding ghost—something like a very old lady's thin hair blown about, and suddenly frozen into immobility, remote and vague; a photograph of the smoke of artillery fire, a long time afterwards, fading away. He means dry weather.

The Cumulus cloud is heaped upwards from a horizontal base, like a pile of massive suds and soap-lathered bubbles: the whole often more or less conical in shape, and with each of the many upper surfaces convex:

He lives at perhaps five thousand feet, and is associated in my mind with Prospero, for no reason that I can discover. The cloud-capp'd towers, the gorgeous palaces, the solemn temples, the great globe itself—and even the strong-based promontories—have no relation to clouds, unless a subconscious one. The Cumulus cloud also means fair weather.

Stratus clouds are more or less fogs. If you can imagine a mist that you have looked down on, raised to about 3,000 feet and looked up at or along at, this is a good picture of stratus. They are vast horizontal sheets, heavier below, and mean about the same in relation to the weather as a fog does. I can only attempt to draw them like this:

CIRRUS

CUMULUS

STRATUS

NIMBUS

TW

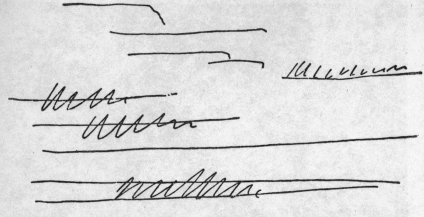

The last kind, Nimbus, is the villain of the piece. So far as I can see, you can get him at any height, below six thousand, and he is merely a shapeless blur.

Grey, whispy, formless, mobile, he draggles about the sky, bringing rain or snow, and all his unions with other kinds of cloud seem to produce progeny as unpleasant as himself.

These four main kinds have bastards, as I said before. A cloud which is not quite Cirrus and not quite Cumulus will be Cirro-Cumulus, and so on. The wicked bastards, like Edmund, are Cirro-Stratus, Alto-Stratus and Cumulo-Nimbus.

Cirro-Stratus is easy to recognise: he is the very high one that looks like sea-rippled sand. Alto-Stratus looks as if the whitish sky-face had gone curdled: he is about half the height of his half-brother. Cumulo-Nimbus is good son Cumulus gone wrong. You can distinguish the traits of decency, the honest soap-suddy cumulus expression flitting across his face: but above the firm, good shoulder there is a betraying wisp, and below he has gone blurred with the curse of the house of Nimbus.

Now all this is backed by a close study of an out-of-date Encyclopaedia Britannica, but as far as weather-wisdom is concerned, it can be put more succinctly. *Safe* clouds are high mare's tails, lamb's tails ('like flocks to feed in air'), soap-suds, or well defined solid loaves that have risen and boiled over a bit. *Unsafe* clouds are sea-rippled, curdled or cream-cheesy, and low, vague, misty puffs. A further and still simpler rule about the weather (like Street's adage about rain coming when the wind is veering anti-clock-wise) is that clouds which live *separately* in the sky mean dry weather, and clouds which extend, run into each other, or *cover* the sky, mean wet.

There are many other simple rules about the weather, for those who cannot rise to be connoisseurs of clouds. The easiest and the least fallible depends on dew. If there is a good dew in the summer there won't be rain, and vice versa. Then there is the effect on the animal creation, the birds and beasts and plants. If the birds, the swifts, rooks and hawks particularly, fly high and far, then you can expect fine weather. It is as if things got lively in advance.★ Bats and field-mice come out quickly after sunset: chick-weed expands its leaves more fully.

On the other hand, if your own senses become sharpened it generally means wet. Thus country people should redouble their efforts at harvest if they can hear distant railways, smell extensively, or see clearly far.

Primed with all this wisdom I asked Tom Bourne how

★It even works on human beings. For instance, 'Do business when the wind is in the north-west.' You will find your buyer more affable.

he predicted disaster during harvest, and he replied: 'When the wind comes from Gorble Farm, it's going to rain.'

28. viii. xxxiv.

To-day we rose at 4.30 again. But only one duck turned up, which I did not get a shot at. We took Luke Fieldfare: so it was a pity it was a dud day. Why? Bright moon last night. Had they come over before 4.30, by moonlight? Or are they permanently scared till the first heavy frost? I shot a bunny, and was pleased about this, as I shall always be by every shot of mine that kills. This is the great advantage of being a bad shot.

1. ix. xxxiv.

I was invited to shoot at Gallowglass, walking. There were eight guns, and I was at the end of the line, between Peter and Charles. We started at 10, but I didn't get a shot till about 11.30. Then Harry, Colonel Southcote, an unknown, and myself lined a hedge, with John on the other side of a narrow spinney at the bottom of it. The rest walked two fields towards us. They sent over a covey of about 40, at Harry's end of the line. I am not sure whether he fired, but at any rate he did not get one. They swung down the hedge. The colonel browned them, missing with both barrels. This spread them. Anonymous missed with both barrels. The air was full of them, like a handful of thrown clods. I picked the birds and startled myself out of my wits by getting a left and right.

It was the first shot at partridges on the first day of the season. The hand shook which evicted the cartridges and I couldn't help making an embryo war-dance, walking in two quick circles. A little after, a covey of seven got up in a stubble field, by the keeper on my left. They swung across. I had my first barrel killed, and the second hard hit. Peter missed. Then nothing till lunch. Then nothing till 4.30, except that I missed two rabbits—confused by dogs, cows and too many guns. But I had better face it and admit that I could never kill a rabbit. At 4.30 we met the big covey again, right at my feet. I killed two with my first barrel, one with my second. The rest of the day we walked roots, up and draw-back empty. I had a chance at two birds. The first was a silly miss in a long cross-shot. I shot behind him. The second was slain between myself and the twins. I don't like walking close, as it is difficult to decide whose bird it is, and I get flurried.

Finally I ended up by failing to kill a very high pigeon, and at that moment two partridges came over the hedge, with the wind, to find me with an empty gun.

We had 13 brace of partridges, about six of rabbits and a brace of hares. Harry had four brace. Peter had a brace and a hare, plus rabbits.

It was a lovely day, bright with hundreds of small well-shaped September clouds, and a thunderstorm in the evening.

Shooting is a pleasure which depends largely on the moods of the country. It comes, too, at a time of the year when men begin to feel a call upon their resources. There is a nip in the air and one can detect the winter coming. So it is a call to endurance, a bracing challenge which makes life far more virile than the supposed provocation of the townsman's spring. In the winter people are in general much more convivial, much more strenuously red-blooded, than they are while the sun vitiates them. And yet the sun is pleasant. In September, over the crackling stubbles, the two seasons meet. One can look back with gratitude to the cow's tail swishing in July, and forward with sanguine expectation to the swing of a horse's rump, as he lifts you over timber.

3. ix. xxxiv.

Visiting Williams to-day, I found him dipping his
sheep. It is an amusing affair. Sheep, along with chickens
and frogs, are creatures for whom I have little respect, and
it was fascinating to watch them being dolloped into the
filthy arsenic. In they go, with all four legs waving and a
ridiculous splash. They regain some sort of equilibrium,
with frantic wriggles, and scuttle for freedom up the sloping side, only to be caught dexterously by means of a kind
of boat-hook and soundly ducked. Souse, souse, clatter
and splash, up she comes and down she goes. I always
hated bullying, but there is something profoundly satisfactory about this. It combines the joys of playing with
water, with the satisfaction of getting one's own back on
an idiot. The men themselves enjoyed it.

I sat up with Williams early this year, in February I think
it was, till three in the morning whilst they were lambing.
He is a first-rate person, the kind of Welshman who
grapples his friends with hoops of steel. Generous and
hospitable, he is an enemy once slighted who throws an
equally tenacious exuberance into his feuds: a genuine
person. He has a feud on at present which gives him more
pleasure than anything in his life, and it will be a pity if he
ever loses it. Not that he will. He will continue to plague
his wicked neighbour, with actions over nettles and rights
of way and the clearing of fallen trees, with passionate glee
until his dying day. Not that he is ever likely to die, or, if
dead, leave go. He will haunt the foe with nettles still.

4. ix. xxxiv.

I am fortunate in my shire friends. I can't think of a
farmer, out of all the many handshakes on Tuesdays,
market day, whose hand doesn't come from his heart. Nor
of one who is not a perfect individual. Williams, with his
Welsh vitality, dresses himself like a scarecrow out of

cussedness, to shew that he calls no man master. If William Williams is good enough for me, well and good: if not, I may go and stick myself on the wall.

I found him in his new gravel pit to-day, and he said to me, in effect: 'Well, my fine gentleman, I see you peering down at me over the rim of this pit, and very neat and tidy you do look: but I wonder what sort of a shewing you would make, if you came down to do a turn of work.' So I took the wind out of his sails by taking off my coat and joining the line; myself with a pick and shovel at the cliff face, Williams at the sieve, and Arch on the cart. And I kept them busy till dinner.

5. ix. xxxiv.

Then there is Luke Fieldfare, the best type of a sporting farmer. He had his left hand wrecked in the war, and now wears it in a leather glove—or a black one at dances. For the first two years after the war he thought he was hopeless, and stood at the front door to watch the hounds go by. For a person who had always hunted and shot, a person who is now on the Warden committee, it must have been terrible. One day his foreman remarked upon the partridges in the roots. Something in the remark was too much for him. Luke went home with a desperate heart, and practised on starlings secretly with one hand. It seemed possible. He sent for the foreman after a few days, and they went to the roots together, the foreman dubious and disapproving. They put up a brace, and Luke swung his gun with his one hand, and killed them left and right.

After that he shot for two years one-handed, and now uses the bad arm as a sort of prop. Probably he is the best local shot. He hunts again, with the reins in his right hand, or tucked under his left arm for emergencies like opening a gate: and I doubt whether half the followers of the Warden hounds have ever noticed his affliction.

Luke knows the Shire country like a hunt servant, and to

hear him describing the day's run for twenty minutes on
end is a pure joy. I have never seen him anything but
cheerful, and young: a wiry sportsman, without an ounce
of fat: a sort of working terrier of a man. He has the
pleasantly dependable habit of being an hour late for
everything.

6. ix. xxxiv.

Finally Tom Bourne, the dearest person in the Shire.
Some tattler told me that when he was a young man he
borrowed the money to buy his farm, off his mother.
Then, with one man to help him, he disappeared from
human knowledge for two years. At the end of that time
he emerged with the money to pay his mother, and the
farm was his. It is the most beautiful farm in the neighbourhood, a red brick cosy, nestling in its orchard and
garden at the top of a hill. He gives me plums (he always
gives) warm from the south wall, and home-brewed ale,
from stupendous barrels in the cold cellar. There is a
difference between home-brewed and the stuff you buy in
pubs. It tastes thin and bitter at first, as if it were ordinary
beer gone sour. Then you identify an intentional edge, a
cidery reminiscence, and soon you are drinking it like a
fish.

Tom's nicest peculiarity, apart from a face like Jack
Hulbert's gone rosy, apart from a sense of humour and
mimicry that would shame Jack Hulbert, and leaving aside
his affectionate hospitality that bullies down any attempt
to refuse his favours, is that he enjoys doing things. It is
grand to watch him starting the petrol engine for the
pump, or harling a dead rabbit, or muzzling a ferret with
string, or liming a field, or washing his hands; because his
fingers are deft and experimental. They enjoy the best way
of doing any job, whether it is a job connected with sport
or a job connected with the water supply. He has that
lovely trait of a carpenter, the trait of enjoying invention;

he seeks empirically for the 'best way' to make something efficient, to repair with anything handy, a twig, a pen-knife, or a bit of string.

So he is never unhappy, never bored by the routine of farming and anxious to get out with his gun. In fact, he is a worker because he loves it. His whole face has smiled itself into a happy bay between nose and chin, so that he can't help smiling, even when he is sorry for himself; and I have long since given up making any attempt to refuse the fruit, the invitations to tea, the liquor, or the presents of game, which he irresistibly thrusts upon me.

9. ix. xxxiv.

One can get a lot of pleasure out of farming, if one isn't a farmer. Probably the happiest person on a farm is the labourer, so long as he does his work well, who does not need to sink and defend his capital. If he works well, then he will enjoy it. The fly in his ointment is the possibility of dismissal. I am neither a farmer nor a farm labourer, and so my work on the land is pure joy. Tom Bourne lets me use Three Woods Farm as a sort of playground, in and out of the shooting season: so that I feel a cupboard love for him, as I did for my grandparents, who spoiled me too. This week I have built a rick with Mark, and been left alone with it for ten exciting minutes, while they were threshing: kept up with Tom in the mowing of thistles over three big fields: had the acute pleasure of smearing ninety sheep, lambs, theaves and ewes, with red paint, in picking them for Shireham sheep fair. But the summum bonum, the excitement to which all these honest joys were a kind of preliminary, like labouring seven years for the man in the Scriptures in order to marry his daughter, happened to-day: when I learned to plough. It was only with a tractor, but it was a rapture that lasted from two o'clock until it was too dark to see. Then they had to fetch me away. Ploughing with a tractor is easy and soporific, but just sufficiently eventful to keep you between life and sleep. You must keep your offside wheel in the furrow and calculate your turns. The moment of throwing in the plough, with a crash, gives you a mild pleasure of decision, accomplishment, truth. It is Right, the thing that confuses the devils, to achieve a good turn covering all the ground: and the coulters clash to work with the iron noise that Chesterton approved of—Crétiens ont droict et Païens ont tort. The noise of the engine is terrific, and the seat leaps like a cantering horse, so that you have a sore tail next day. I had one of my rare baths this evening and inspected honourable wounds: the left hand raw from jerking on the rope to drop the plough and the right shin bruised by its clutch, a big toe cracked by a shooting boot, the right hand blistered on the rick. But these were glorious scars to an amateur, recollections of triumph: and when it was tender sitting on the hard enamel I could look back over my first acre and more of Shire earth—the two ploughshares threw it up like the forefoot of a ship on land, the dry-rhubarb-powder bursting out of England, leaping alive, and to-be-fruitful.

10. ix. xxxiv.

Well, no amount of mal-administration and concentration on the industrial wens can take away their *niceness* from our farmers, even if they are doomed to be ruined. There is old Tommy Baily, whom I meet shooting. He is reputed to be very rich, certainly is very shy, and cares for nothing but hares. Partridges he absent-mindedly shoots at, sometimes hit and sometimes miss, as he wanders diffidently along. But let him see a hare, and watch the difference. He shoots with nothing but fours, because he doesn't mind about the wing game but does about the fur, and occasionally he leaves the line altogether, striking out on a reconnaissance of his own, unable to pass over a 'hairy' adjacent piece of country.

Then there is Watson, a heavy man with a Daimler and a shoot in Norfolk, who goes home from our little skirmishes contemptuously, if it begins to rain. And there is Tilly, who doesn't shoot because he saw a relation killed in a gun accident when he was young, but who loves the hounds and walks their puppies for them, always a damned nuisance, with an embarrassing devotion. And Frank Derby, looking faintly disapproving and as if he were worrying about something else, but as nice as nice could be. And Wilson greedy for profit, and John Brown working like a nigger without hope of making any, and Secker sanguine for his own ends.

These, together with the publicans and the policemen and the farm labourers and the road menders, greet one on market day. It is a grand day. Everybody is there that matters, all one's friends and no enemies, and the pubs don't close. There is the indefinable excitement of purchase and bargain in the air, and the quick eye and movements of the auctioneer, and the bleating of sheep, and the clinking of glasses, and all sorts of queer things to buy in pens or on stalls, and a general air of celerity in the town itself, so that one can tell 'this is market day' without knowing the day of the week.

11. ix. xxxiv.

We shot over Williams: one of the nicest days. I heard rumours of what was to be expected, from Bourne, after accepting. I was afraid that they were going to shoot pheasants (which they were) and lodged a strong, tactful protest at the first opportunity. To Williams' immortal credit, he thereafter discouraged it. What a circus! Any keen policeman would have run us in at sight. One man was completely round, a sort of perambulating carbuncle, and one had a vermilion nose, and one looked like Pistol. The first thing Williams did was to clean his gun, with a pull through, that hadn't been cleaned since he shot last year. Then we set out, at about 2 o'clock.

The place was thick with birds. I think we saw 200. Everybody was in command, everybody pointed his gun at me, nobody did more than put his safety catch on, even if he was climbing through a blackthorn, and the wings were generally about 20 yards behind the centre. The keenness was high. One charged off in any direction that took one's fancy. Williams, the excitable Welsh angel, never saw a covey but what he wanted to follow it wherever it was going, at once. There were the sheep dogs that charged about in all directions whenever a gun was fired off. At one stage two people had been left (abandoned without notice, after being placed for a drive which was dropped at the last moment) half a mile behind; three more, myself included, were lying on our backs in a valley; and Williams, with other ebullient spirits, was crawling about in a bed of bulrushes, some hundreds of yards ahead. I was furiously angry, resigned, amused, delighted, by turns, and shot like an idiot, but that didn't matter.

We had nine brace (including one young pheasant by mistake) and a few rabbits. There were seven guns. I had a brace and a half to hand, one shared, and a wounded brace never picked. There was never time to pick anything. I missed the easiest shots I had, but it was a splendid day. One high just shootable partridge went right down the line unscathed, drawing 10 cartridges. My only decent shot was a close bird, that had to be taken close, or else somebody else would have had him or me, whose head I blew almost off.

I remember hitting a bird which looked as if it had had blown up (the feathers), but was never picked; walking a large field of stubble with my right-hand neighbour's gun pointing at the pit of my stomach; deciding never to invite Secker (who shot the pheasant) over my own land, but breaking that resolve; refraining with difficulty from shooting Williams, who suddenly drove his car down the edge of a full field of roots, shouting in a stentorian voice, 'Where are they?'; missing the easiest shot of my life, and the most difficult, and two of the oddest; the fact that practically none of the party could button up their waistcoats on the right buttons; a really masterly drive (organised by me—in temporary though divided command) being ruined by the other wing (which wouldn't stop) and forcing me to fire at a covey of about 40 (which would, if the other wing had stopped, have swung right down the line) when crouching half-way through a barbed-wire fence with a barb in my behind (the bird turned and was not picked); and Williams' amazingly hospitable high tea afterwards, everybody lovely and hungry and only one tie between the lot of us. I don't know when I enjoyed a day more, taking it bye and large. Jimmy Warm shot his first partridge, with tremendous secret joy, just breaking silence. There was an early-morning mist and all was piping hot. To-morrow is the first day over half my own little rough territory. I shall have to say my prayers to-night.

Brown retrieved her first bird. She has been a trouble, and is going to be.

12. ix. xxxiv.

I woke up with a pain in the top of my belly—some form of indigestion, I suppose—and had to rush about with the final arrangements of telephoning and luncheon, before I went up early to Wood Fields.

The place is of 500 acres (37 woodland, and I should think a good 50 arable). The shooting shared between me and Mr. Bourne. I pay next to nothing, and we split the game and rabbits, and Tom has the reasonable option of shooting when I do.

Harry Southcote and Jimmy Warm arrived at 10.20, and we pushed off with four guns. We killed a rabbit and a brace of partridges skirting the N.E. boundary, myself on the boundary wing, well forward. Luke Fieldfare (late as usual) found us when we were on the Close boundary. We swung round the plough stubble, and reached the roots without seeing anything.

The roots shewed some birds—say 50. I got a brace on the right wing.

Fieldfare's brother-in-law, Aytoun, turned up at about noon, and somewhere about that time Tom Bourne went off to Camford. This left us four guns, counting Jimmy. We had three dogs, a blind labrador belonging to Ayton, Fieldfare's spaniel, and Brown. With this contingent, now that we knew what was what, we set out to do business. At about 1.30 we decided to give the Wood Field's roots a rest (we had combined walk and drive about 3 times across them) and paid a flying visit to the other territory.

This consists of the farms of Wilson (150 acres at the Old Inn, half—almost—arable), Tilly at Chackford (250 acres), and Robins towards Park (70 acres).

We just took the stubble and roots of these, once through, and fetched a brace off each, with one over. I had a tremendous high shot in Wilson's on the left wing, a miracle.

We had a dust up before going back to Bourne's. So much necessary humility in learning to fly has made me autocratic on the rebound; and in any case autocracy is essential in the shooting field. It is the same as an army; and shooting, like all joys, is a serious business. It was a grand day at Williams', because I did not have to feel responsible for making a show of birds. As a guest one can afford to be irresponsible. As a host it becomes an altogether different business, because the sport depends upon oneself. And if it is to be good sport, it has got to be controlled. However unimportant the shoot may be, it is worth running it with discipline, so as to kill more birds. In this way the legendary colonel, with a high blood-pressure, who has a fit if a gun gets a foot out of line, is worth having as a host.

Anyway, I came back, right or wrong, with a chastened line. It was over an illicit rest for beer; and I am now faintly ashamed of having made a fuss.

In Wood Fields we didn't do much more. The day ended, to all intents and purposes, with four birds down between Harry Southcote, Luke Fieldfare and myself—of which I felt inclined to claim left and right, one shared.

We ended with 11½ brace, a brace of pigeons, a hare and some rabbits. I am satisfied with this: for it was practically speaking to four guns. Harry Southcote shot beautifully, getting 4½ brace.

Aytoun shot with a 28 bore. He is the best shot that I meet among the farmers, although he is not a farmer and not local. An ideal shooting companion, he relishes walking on the wings and kills scientifically and never counts or claims his birds, and is always in a sunny humour and doesn't spoil his quite remarkable dog. It would be nice to have a world of one's own and pick this kind of person to live in it.

Harry Southcote was walked off his vaunted feet when we stopped, and had to beg for mercy.

Brown hunted a runner, quartering exquisitely, and picked it up, and more or less brought it to hand. I climbed a fence and patted and cheered her: which, I believe, was wrong.

The birds were wild, the cover inadequate, and there was no close shooting.

I put up 5 hen pheasants.

I think on the whole the host gets more fun out of a shooting party. Although the worries are trebled for him, the corresponding delights of strategy and tactics amply make up for them. Just as it is a real tragedy to see a covey go sideways out of a drive, so is it a real delight to see one's plans work out. If there were ever any sensitive and intelligent generals during the war, I believe they must have sampled the depths, but also the peaks of human achievement. One is being a general, on the humaner scale: pitting

one's wits against the animal kingdom: balancing wind,
weather, season, habit and experience against one another.
Also it is pleasant, as Sancho Panza remarked, to have
command—even over a flock of sheep. It is exciting to ask
opinion, but not to tolerate it unless asked, and to match it
up in one's own mind, and to accept responsibility.

13. ix. xxxiv.

There is something of the old Shire foresters in the
friends who invite me to shoot and entertain me with their
independent hospitality. The man who built old Silston
church was called Kelly. He was unequalled at boxing,
fencing and poaching foxes: he was in league with the
Devil, and could haunt old ladies. When he died he
directed that his grave should be covered with oak planks
covered with sharp spikes. Nobody had trodden on him
whilst he was alive, and he did not propose to be trodden
in the grave. I can see a bit of Williams in old Kelly. He
wrote his own epitaph:

> 'Weep not for me, for that were vain;
> Weep for yourself and then refrain.'

14. ix. xxxiv.

It is a comfort to feel pleasure in meeting people, so that
you hasten together for a few friendly words, even if there
is no business to be done. One transfers one's little bits of
country news on market day, and one's friends go home to
their wives and mention the meeting, and life is full of the
small important things.

Another thing which gives me very great pleasure is the
fact that I can't drive past a gang of road menders in a
radius of five miles without waving and grinning to
Nugget, or Sam, or Fred. And then they all yell like
demons, and scream to me to 'let her go,' and I have to roar

up to sixty in third gear, vanishing in a cloud of dust and amusement and congratulation.

15. ix. xxxiv.

We shot over Luke Fieldfare's—five guns. It was a sweltering day with thunderstorms going on all round us in the afternoon. A gun is a frightening thing to carry in a thunderstorm, for a person that is sin-conscious.

I am terrified of thunderstorms, principally from an early consciousness that if Jupiter did distribute his thunderbolts on inverted merit I should be one of the first recipients. Also, as an accomplished water-diviner, I believe thunder has a particular effect upon me. It makes me nervous like a cat, so that shooting or golf or fishing or anything that has iron or wetness or the property of sticking up becomes a burden. I would lief put down my gun in the best drive, and lie on my face in the middle of a field, except that it would be worse to be laughed at.

We killed eight brace of partridges, with 5 hares, a pigeon and a rabbit. I was still out of sorts and sweated till I looked as if I had been buttered, walking the wing with Fred Aytoun, to get exercise. The centre never gave us time to get forward. Luke went sensibly, but not firm enough with the other two farmers—who charged ahead, as farmers sometimes do. I did not shoot well, but not foully: killed a brace and a half, all single birds coming fast diagonally, and a high pigeon who thought he was out of range, and the rabbit—the last shot of the day. I had two things to reproach myself. One was a lovely close covey of seven, which might have given me three birds with luck, by picking the first two close together: I think a legitimate practice. But I got muddled with my safety catch, and this wrecked the whole thing. The other was a covey sent over by the centre when Aytoun and I were on the other side of a high hedge. They had not given us time to get forward and we were running like hell to get into position when

they came over. There was some excuse for missing them,
since nobody fires at his best in the middle of a canter; but
still I felt annoyed. I also missed two single driven birds,
and shared a hare. Not much of a share, since he was finally
run down by Fred's blind black labrador (Belle or Mother)
after eight barrels. Fred had a beautiful left and right, with
his 28 bore, out of the covey that I missed with my safety
catch.

Luke shoots well, but I have not seen him get a left and
right. He got a beautiful long hare. I fire behind ground
game, and wish I could get over it. Also one ought to make
up one's mind about cartridges and stick to them. The
difference between Pegamoid, Primax and Remington's
Kleenbore is real, and it is misleading to mix them up. If I
could afford it I would use nothing but Pegamoid 5½
shot.

Two of mine were satisfactory. The solitary pigeon
coming a cropper out of a great deal of air twenty yards
behind a man on my right; and the last driven partridge,
single, swishing along low on the other side of a hedge by a
rick, and coming into the hedge with a rumple.

Brown disgraced herself in the morning, hunting my
first easy bird quite wildly, and I took her home. I suppose
I shouldn't have tried an uneducated setter as a retriever so
early in the day.

I consoled myself for having to run all the time on the
wings, by reciting Shakespeare:

> 'Double double,
> Toil and trouble.'

16. ix. xxxiv.

Water-divining is not a rare faculty. I seldom meet
anybody who cannot do it, once they have been nursed
along with a little encouragement. You must hold your
forked twig tightly, and put your thumbs over the cut
ends. This concentrated magnetic contact is important.
The only other important thing for the beginner is not to

move too quickly. Stand still until you are accustomed to the position, and then move cautiously, a step at a time. The arms are taut in front of you, palms upwards, and the fork vertical. It is ten to one that the twig will soon begin to bow (in my case it comes towards me) and no amount of effort will hold it still—unless you relax the position. You can hold it so tight that it snaps, or twists its bark off, but come it will.

17. ix. xxxiv.

We shot over a farm at Southam, belonging to the Derbys. They are giving it up on the 29th, and want everything killed before then.

The 29th is New Michaelmas Day, the date on which farm leases expire. It is one of the regular dates of the country year in the Shire, like the 15th of May for shooting rooks or the Easter Bank holiday for planting potatoes in the allotments. You don't get a rook pie often nowadays, yet it is very nice. The birds are skinned, not plucked, and only the legs and breasts are used, along with all sorts of tasty additions like onions and eggs.

We started at 1.30. Luke Fieldfare, Frank Derby, John Brown, Watson, a clergyman, and myself. The clergyman was a magnificent surprise, a voice so fruity and ecclesiastical that he continuously seemed to be imitating himself. He was not in a clerical collar and we did not watch his name. On being introduced to Luke, a church-warden, he said: 'Ay think ay've already maide your acquaintance at the archi-diaconal visitaytions.' Luke said: 'What?' The cleric said: 'At the archi-diaconal visitaytions.' Luke said: 'Where the hell's that?' To which the clergyman replied: 'Yew wouldn't say that to the Bis-hop.' This was a good start.

First of all the shooting was rather a circus, only the clergyman was worse. We careered about and the birds were as wild as we were, so we never got up to anything

before the church had sent it away. He generally popped
up in front of a line of walking guns and said: 'All the birds
have flown away. Ay can't think whay.' In the end we
lined for a drive. I got a left and right, but one was a runner
who was not picked through running down a rabbit hole
in view. Then it began to pour. It rained as if it never
would stop, and Luke was in the middle of a vast field
trying to pick a wounded bird and the rest of us stood
under a hedge talking about ecclesiastical matters. After
hours of this John Brown and Watson decided to pack up. I
think we only had 1½ brace.

Luke and Frank Derby wanted to stop, but were not
convinced. The clergyman, who was evidently a very
valuable person, wanted to go on—we were far too wet
for it to make any difference—and I lay low, determined to
put off the parting as late as possible. Brown and Watson
definitely went. Luke tried to, but we kept him in the car
drinking beer. After half an hour it looked as if it just
might clear, so we waited.

To be rewarded by a brilliant evening, with 7 brace of
partridges, 4 hares and 13 rabbits. Of these I killed 2 brace,
a hare, 4 rabbits, and walked the wing all day in prodigious
manoeuvres.

Luke got his first left and right that I have seen to-day.
Frank Derby was mad on hares, and would suddenly
break the line, and dart away with his gun at the high port,
and chase them for miles. I was pleased with my hare,
stone dead in a flabby somersault and a cloud of moisture,
and my rabbits. Ground game improves.

18. ix. xxxiv.

I suddenly had a bye-day over my own territory, at
about two hours' notice. We started at 3 in the afternoon,
after I had spent the whole morning trying to get
Williams, Derby, Secker, Brown, Watson, or anybody
else to come. But it was market day; and there was some

sort of sale in the neighbourhood in the afternoon. So they all refused. At any rate, they can't say I haven't asked them back, and it has been a good thing in a way. We started at 3, an amazing collection of marksmen. There was Major Ninton, and his son walking, Jimmy Warm, Tom O'Connel, Allweather (the sergeant) and myself. At about 5 o'clock Mr. Bourne joined up over his land. Birds were scarce and wild in the east. But we ought to have had 3 brace there. Nobody hit one at all, though the major just hit me, from the opposite end of a very long line.

At Bourne's the marksmanship improved slightly, but the generalship declined. I left Bourne to do our second and third drives, driving to self and Ninton and Jimmy, and somebody spoilt them—thereafter blaming Tom O'Connel. The latter must have had a sad day. He was slightly browbeaten by me, for not shooting at birds at 25 yards: he missed everything: he was rated by Tom for spoiling the drive, which as a matter of fact had been equally spoilt by all the walkers: and he ended by spraining his ankle. I gave him a hare and Ninton took him home.

But to get back to Bourne's. We put a good 40–60 out of the roots, and the sergeant got 2 by browning and Tom missed, and Jimmy was too shy to fire. I killed a hare. The drive through the famous holding grass field then took place, under mismanagement, and yielded a solitary frenchman, who came over about 50 yards to my left and I killed him by luck. Then I went to turn them at the hedge between two poor fields, whilst the guns swung inefficiently round a third. Here everybody blazed away at hares, and the sergeant killed one. We then went round again, and I spoilt the manoeuvre myself, by not going right round the plough, and lost the birds to our right. I had also missed both barrels in the east. Total bag: 2 brace, 2 hares, 1 rabbit. It ought to have been seven brace (to ten if Tom Bourne's drive had come off). My main recollections are of people not firing when they might have done, and of blaspheming audibly.

But I have paid off my invitations, and learnt a lot. You don't enjoy the smooth without the rough; and this shoot is certainly that.

The sergeant is good to watch. Ready—Present—FIRE! He looks as if he was bayoneting Germans.

19. ix. xxxiv.

I love living in the country, and am profoundly thankful that I don't like living in towns. As the French lady said about spinach: 'I'm glad I don't like spinach, because if I did like it I should eat it in large quantities; and it is detestable stuff.'

20. ix. xxxiv.

I should like to write a book in praise of liquor. I don't see why plain water should be excluded, if it comes in your hand or hat directly from a quick stream, or if you lie down on the bank and drink without intermediary. Somebody or other in the Bible got crossed off for his direct drinking, one of the more notable examples of the wrong-headedness of Jehovah. But of course the main part would be devoted to intoxicants: of which the kings are gin and beer. Nobody can be surprised to learn from Jefferies that gin is the best unguent for the locks of guns—it is not too heavy, and doesn't get solid with the cold. It is good for the kidneys, and probably for everything else. I shouldn't be surprised if it were good for mixing with oil paints, or cleaning the windscreen of a car, or polishing buttons, or curing whooping cough, or mending china. The philosophers used gold medicinally, just as they did pearls. It comes to this, that all really valuable things are good for everything.

The encyclopaedia would have to include several chapters on opening bottles without corkscrews, a feat which I am proud to be able to perform in two ways, and on the manufacture of love-potions from the root of the orchis.

21. ix. xxxiv.

I suppose one has to be desperate, to be a successful writer. One has to reach a rock-bottom at which one can afford to let everything go hang. One has got to damn the public, chance one's living, say what one thinks, and be oneself. Then something may come out.

But I am afraid to do this. I haven't the courage to chance starvation, and so I try to serve God and Mammon. I try to write 'proper' books, which fizzle out for their propriety, when all the time there are other things that I should like to say and honester ways to say them. I was lamenting this to a friend of mine who is a burglar, but he answered: 'You can't starve. All you have to do is try burglary. If you get away with it you have money; and if you are caught they give you food in prison.'

26. ix. xxxiv.

We had half a day over Derby's. The church was again represented and behaved as usual—a grand person. There were also Frank Derby, John Brown, Watson, Luke Field-fare, self, and five beaters. We got 4½ brace, 3 hares, 11 rabbits. Of these I had 1½ brace and an odd one picked up running ten minutes after a drive, which I suspect was mine from its position. But I am sick of shooting jealous. It is one of the things which don't seem worth wrangling about. It is worth being proud of what one does, but only when it does not admit of question, as in fishing. Good resolution from this day forth: never to claim a bird, even if there is no doubt at all. It would be nice not even to keep count of one's birds, but I don't think I can rise to this obviously proper attitude yet.

The wind was amazing. I should think it was a gale nearly; at any rate the wireless had a gale warning last night, and the birds came over like bullets, streaming with the wind. Everybody was missing like hell, including Luke. Although I managed to get two of the driven birds, one of them a single straggler, I was shooting ill. I missed two easy shots, also a rabbit. Proh dolor!

Old John Brown, the ground game shooter who leaves the birds severely alone and shoots with number fours, wreaks great havoc among the rabbits. He canters along in a rather aimless way, and to-day wiped Watson's eye most beautifully—killing a hare that I should have left alone (and I seem to take things up to 70 yards) with one barrel, after Watson had missed quite close with two. Watson had shot at a sitting hare scandalously, and missed it, so I was delighted.

But what a wind! You could scarcely tell they were partridges before they were gone.

It poured at the end, a thin driving shower, and my twa-snooted bonnet was worth its weight in salmon. Luke said to me: 'You'll be able to circumvent them to-day, they won't know whether you're coming or going.' I said: 'Yes, and if only I was a clergyman I could wear my collar back to front as well.' But the church didn't mind He shot a rabbit eventually.

27. ix. xxxiv.

Jimmy Warm scored 180 with three darts last night, the first time I have seen it done. You get a lot of people who talk of having done it or seen it, but the actual occurrence is rare, except on a 'landlord's' board. I wrote the score, and the date, and the principal's name, on the ceiling.*

*I performed this feat myself, on the 18th of August, 1935, for the first and last time in three or four thousand games of darts, at a public house called the Rose and Crown, in Burwash: and put my own name in the same proud position. It was not a landlord's board.

The games played in the public houses vary with the locality. Shove-penny is commoner in the south of England than elsewhere; darts centre on the metropolis and begin to fade at about a hundred and fifty miles away from it; skittles is sporadic; in the west they play a ring game which entails dropping rings on a horizontal board; in the east the dart-board assumes curious variations, sometimes without a treble ring, sometimes with triangles instead of rings, and sometimes with circles. The size of the double and treble rings vary. When the rings are wide it is easier to score on them, and the games are finished more quickly. Since at least two half-pints of beer are sold as the result of every game, it means that the beer gets sold quicker on a wide-ringed board. This kind is therefore called a 'landlord's' board: it pays him to have one.

The rules of common darts vary as much as the boards on which the game is played. I suppose there must be some Affiliated Co-operative Limited Gilt-Edged Ultimate Wenman's Exclusive Divinely Inspired Dart Association in London (where heavy metal darts are thrown, as opposed to the feathered darts of the country) and that these cockneys issue an authoritative booklet of their own rules to any degenerate publican who chooses to observe them. The booklet will itself, I suspect, be published by a brewing or tobacco firm as an advertisement for their own goods. We in Tenmere prefer to observe our own rules.

A dart-board consists of two narrow concentric circles intersected by twenty segments.

Each of these twenty segments is numbered according to a fascinating mathematical formula, which I am unable to work out, so that a high number so far as possible is next to a low number, and so that the even and odd numbers are properly balanced round the board. Any dart that lodges in the segment called 20 counts 20; but if it lodges in the part of the segment intersected by the narrow outer circle it counts twice twenty, and if in the part intersected by the narrow inner circle it counts three times twenty. So the

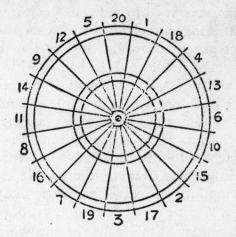

outer ring is called the Double Ring, and the inner ring is
called the Treble. In the very centre of the board there is a
tiny circle (counting 50) surrounded by another circle
counting 25; but these are rarely used.

I have played seven kinds of game on this board, and
there must be many other variants, but the two best games
are ordinary Darts and Shanghai.

In ordinary darts you must score exactly 301, beginning
and finishing in the double ring. Thus the perfect player
could win a game in two hands of three darts (the players
throw three darts each, in turn) by scoring thus:

First dart, *double* 20	—	40
Second dart, treble 20	—	60
Third dart, treble 20	—	60
		— Other man throws.
Fourth dart, treble 20	—	60
Fifth dart, treble 19	—	57
Sixth dart, *double* 12	—	24
		301

Nothing counts at all until you have got a dart into the double ring to begin with, and your last dart has got to be a double that brings your score to 301 exactly. This is why my perfect player threw his fifth dart at the treble 19, instead of at the treble 20. If he had failed to switch from even numbers to odd ones he would have been in a mess. Suppose he had gone on at the treble 20, and got it. This would have left him 21, to make the exact 301; and it is not possible to score 21 in a double ring, for it is an odd number. He would then have had to waste another dart in getting a single one (leaving him double 10) or a single three (leaving him double 9) or a single five (leaving him double 8) or a single seven (leaving him double 7) or etc.

The first player to achieve his 301, throwing in turns and tossing for start, is the winner.

Tossing is an art in itself, which I learnt in Gloucestershire. The clientèle of the pub which I patronised in that county would have robbed me of my living teeth for the ivory, as I them, but we were very fond of each other all the same. You had to keep an eye on your glass, if you didn't want to find it empty, and the publican's nickname was Happy. Briefly you can win a toss as an amateur in one of four ways: by feeling the coin in your pocket before you take it out, and putting it down tails upwards (it is a trait of human nature 90% of the time, to call Heads); by using a sixpence, which can be put half down edgeways and then unobtrusively turned in the desired direction after the other man has called; by using two coins, one with the head upwards and the other with the tail, thereafter slipping your hand sideways off the one which has not been called; and finally by allowing your opponent, as if inadvertently, to see the face of the coin in your right hand (say a Head) before turning it over on to the back of your left hand—when he will call Tails. But, by a very simple sleight of hand, you have turned it over again in the air.

In Tenmere we differ from the Wenmen by playing the

best of three games for one drink (this is called Three-O-
One-Legs, or Horses) and by not Busting. Since we don't
Bust, there is no need to explain what Busting is. Nearly
all the numbers have names of their own: 26 is Bed and
Breakfast, or Euston Road (the association being with
2/6); 81 is called Snowstorm (because I believe there was a
blizzard in that year); 66 is Clicketty-Click; 123 is called
Oddfellows; Double 10 is Two Old 'Ens; 62 is While-
Shepherds-Watch, because the hymn of that name is
numbered thus in the local hymn-book; 88 is Connaught
Rangers, because the Rangers were the 88th regiment on
foot; and 111 is known as Nelson, for a delightful reason
that is unfortunately unprintable.

Shanghai is a more accurate game than ordinary darts,
or at least it is harder on inaccuracy. No doubles are
required for start or finish. Each player throws three darts
at the segment one, then three at the segment two, and so
on up to nine. Those darts which arrive in the segment at
which he is throwing score what they are worth, and those
outside it don't score at all. For instance, if I am throwing
at seven and get two in it with one out, then my score for
that figure is 14. Trebles and Doubles count, so that if one
of my two scoring darts happened to be in the treble 7 and
the other in the double 7, my score would be 35 for that
figure. We add up as we go along, and the man with the
largest score at the end wins. There is one magnificent
Bogey that haunts every game of Shanghai, and this is
called Scrubbing. If I don't get any of my three darts into
the segment of the moment, I not only fail to score, but
also lose my whole score up to date: it is scrubbed off the
slate. By the time I reach the number seven, I may have
amassed about 60 points; if I don't manage to score a seven
I lose them all, and start again with no points in hand at
number eight. My outlook is pretty poor (unless I can
score three treble eights and three treble nines—which
would give me 153) and Scrubbing is therefore much
dreaded.

You can also play cricket, Corners, Round the Board, Fifties, and other varieties in Norfolk.

A good gambling variation can be had with a plasticine board. The setter is allowed to stick a sixpenny piece anywhere he likes on the board, and to charge a penny for three darts at it. If the thrower hits the sixpence it becomes his property; or rather he turns into the setter, and collects the pennies (for three darts) from the rest of the field, until he is himself knocked down.

29. ix. xxxiv.

We had half a day over Luke Fieldfare's, driving, killing 16 brace and 3 hares, or it may have been 5. This was an instructive day, when it comes to shooting jealousy. I had 2 brace, and there were nine guns, so that I must have been slightly above the average. But how can one have an average at shooting? The first drive and the second did not give me a shot. I was on the wing. In the third I was in the middle and this was easily the best of the day. The birds came over quicker than one could load. Fred Aytoun, on my right, was missing finely. After about four minutes we had time to breathe and count—a brace each picked, and heaven knows how many poor creatures may have gone away to tower a couple of fields off or with dropped legs. There was no time to look behind. This was the best four minutes this season. The one drive yielded 6 brace to the line. Then there was a drive that showed me nothing on the wing. Then I shot a single bird that swung down the line walking, and thereby wiped an anonymous eye. Then a single bird was presented to me on the wing, and I shot it. Then two more drives showed me nothing. So five drives came to me without a shot. Supposing I had been lucky in my place (and Luke did not place us, but left us to scramble, and I was too much the dirty gentleman to thrust into the middle) I might have had four brace instead of two. Supposing, on the other hand, that I had not been in the middle for the third drive, I should have only had a brace. It seems to me impossible to compare a bag with the next man's, when everything is such a matter of luck. The only sense in counting one's own heads is so that one can add them up at the end of the season.

I remember: getting up at 6 to feed my pheasants, working till 12.30 with grey flannels over my gaiters, arriving at Luke's at 12.38. Also the sousing rain from 3.30 onwards; and borrowing a cape at tea from Charlie's; and finding that it did not impede my firing; and begging a beret from one of his daughters—I had stupidly left the twa-snooted at home—and my single walked up partridge going wallop-and-scramble into the branches of a tree above my head, with a surprised expression; and offering one of the birds I had picked in the third drive to Fred in case he might have fired at it as well, a concession to Wednesday's resolution; and the black tips of a hare's ears.

The nicest parts of a hare are its ears. Not only are they the distinctive and beautiful feature, but they associate themselves with the finest of all sports as well. A Hare's Lug is a good fly, dry or wet, and when you are fishing with its mouldy-looking body you can remember the pricked ears of a real hare in long grass: just as you can remember, when you turn the sandy creature himself over, in a head-shaking somersault, the warm days in the loch ripple, and how you dressed the fly with spittle or mud to make him sink.

30. ix. xxxiv.

There is an unfortunate division between the body and the mind. Perhaps it was always prevalent. Perhaps the first puny anthropoid was the first intelligent one, because he had to be to survive. Naturally he sneered at the brawny ones, and they threw coconuts at him. But it is a fortuitous division none the less. I can think of no intrinsic reason why intelligence should not go with physical efficiency, or why a person should not endeavour to combine the two. The attempt is seldom greeted with applause. My intellectual friends consider my fishing a pose, and my fishing friends have an anxious expression, in case I should say something perverse.

1. x. xxxiv.

The first of October. I got up at 6.15 and went to the home field to see if any pheasants were peeping out of Roof House. The sun was due to rise at 6.45, or something preposterous like that (it is fine to feel condescending towards the sun himself, in respect of early rising), but it was quite light. There were no pheasants. I tried all my outlying coverts—the Renford cabbages, etc.—but nothing. Back for breakfast at nine, and had a fine bath, reading the morning paper, as I was not working till eleven. Then I earned my living till 12.45 and fixed up the riding after luncheon; fed my pheasants; took an intelligent beater to explain the drives at Three Woods; and went by appointment to the Ransomes to slay a cock pheasant who was alleged to inhabit an abandoned kitchen garden. We walked all through the nettles, thistles, grass and dock without putting him up. There were Bill Ransome, Ker, Mrs. R. with an untrained cocker, and myself. We were all wandering rather aimlessly when two hen pheasants that had been sitting tight (with recollections of Williams next door, I suppose) got up in front of Ker—who missed.

They came across me, a beautiful chance for a left and right, but I only hit the front one hard. She threw up her head and went on, scattering feathers into Williams' osiers. I did not expect to see her again, but got over the wall with a vague idea of searching. Just then, whilst I was changing my cartridges, somebody put up the cock, who came straight over my head—a magnificent sight, wings spread, tail streaming high up. By the time I had got some cartridges in, he was at the nadir. I covered him wildly, and pulled, but the safety catch had stayed on in the flurry. So he waits for another day. In a little while Bill brought the cocker to seek dead in the thick osiers. To my astonishment, as well as to everybody else's, she walked straight onto the first hen, stone dead: a magnificent piece of work.

Then I worked again till 5.45, when I tried the verges of Roof House in a rainstorm, and finally back to dinner and to work till 10. To-morrow the cock, and to-day there is a hen's tail feather in the twa-snooted, on the first day of the pheasant season.

Understand me clearly here, however: for it is the duty of parents to give, if they are able, book-learning to their children, having first taken care to make them capable of earning their living by bodily labour.

COBBETT

He could cook, he could sew, he could darn a stocking and milk a cow, he was an efficient wood-cutter and a good hand at embroidery, fires always burned when he had laid them and a floor after he had scrubbed it was thoroughly clean.

ALDOUS HUXLEY ON D. H. LAWRENCE

2 . x . xxxiv .

The curse of England is industry, as Cobbett realised. But who reads Cobbett now? Who knows nowadays which way the wind was blowing when he got up, and whether it has changed since? We are mechanically introverted, unable to see the world about us, unable to cope with it with our hands, even unable to cope with ourselves. It is astonishing to see the intellectuals, who know all about communism and the European situation, trying to live their own lives, even indoors. They lean against the mantelpiece at the wrong angle, and the fender slips, and bang goes one of the candlesticks—broken. They can't cope even with their own centres of gravity. I saw a presumably 'modern' boy the other day, who was so little conscious of the position of his own body that he fell backwards off a chair while thinking of something else.

All truly good and great men are interested in laying and lighting fires. With mature consideration, and plenty of time to examine the problem in all its aspects (scientific, architectural, thermal, physico-chemical and artistic) the noble man can light any fire with one match, so that it not only keeps burning, but begins to burn maturely quite soon. I lit a fire in a cartridge box in Lapland, inside a tent, using only the cores of dead branches, when the stunted forest had been soaked by a north-westerly rain for four hours.

Get your communist to light a fire in an English interior grate. He clumsily lumps on, criss-cross and anyhow, a few random logs and hunks, applies half a dozen matches, and finally has to go for the paraffin: if he has the sense to do that. That a fire should be built like a house; that paraffin, or the modern industrial firelighters made of chemical flummery are an admission of failure; these are matters beyond his taste. I should like to have the salvation of all communists who are dear to me. I should begin with fires, and the course would take about six months.

First we should learn about trees—how to distinguish every possible sort at every season of the year, and which woods were best for what things. Kipling should teach them to use beech for cups, and to fear the elum. When they knew their trees thoroughly, and loved them for themselves, they should cut them up to discover their textures; which woods would light the soonest, which were more tindery, which more like blotting paper, which nearest to the solidity of coal, which heat-giving and which only light. Then there would be a short course in architecture (fires are mainly gothic rather than classical— the pointed arch burns best) and a brief sortie into the rising properties of heat. After that we should have to deal with philosophy, read Cobbett, go for long walks in the country, possibly shoot or fish in it, take a toss over timber, be psychoanalysed, clear up all the problems of life and death and gastronomy. At last we should be ready to approach the pentecost. The acolyte would take a pride in fetching his own coal from the cellar (without falling downstairs, stunning himself with the coal hammer, or losing his way) and in getting his hands properly black—no gloves, tongs or mush. He would light, with one match, his first real fire. How he would wait, with nervousness and trepidation, for those few seconds whilst the kindling fell in and the architecture reconstructed itself! But all would be well. The flames would falter, yellow and heatless, like little kittens; would catch hold evenly and take heart with life. I should set him down before them in an easy-chair, with alcohol and tobacco. He should read me two poems: the one about the coal miners and Wilfred Owen, and Fifty Faggots by Edward Thomas.

3. x. xxxiv.

A good way of naming a day, is to call it by its wind. 'Wednesday' is an impersonal thing, but days are individual. A great deal more than half their individuality depends upon the wind. A good hunting or fishing diary would do better to have a column in which one wrote, for instance: 'A north-westerly day,' rather than the stupid date.

A north-westerly day in spring. The sun bright and clear spaces of the sky a teeming blue; but ice in the quick air, and the clouds, which move rapidly, going from white at the blue-sky edge to a gravid indigo.

The easterly day is an individual, a relentless Borgia searching the townsman's bones; but to those who can stand up to him, in a kind of country equality, a stimulus. He is a pirate; but if you can wear the knife between your teeth also, a boon companion.

So with the other winds, the blusterous, the snow-carrying, the corn-rippling, the becalmed. They make the day. My communist, when he has learnt to meditate upon a fire, shall learn to know the wind. I shall wake him at all hours of the day and night, asking the quarter. When he is a sailor I understand that he will learn not to spit against it; and on land he shall be taught to turn his back towards it when he leaves the country pub.

If he is an aviator, and his passenger in the front seat betrays a tendency to be sick, he will learn to sideslip to the opposite side.

4. x. xxxiv.

Physical clumsiness annoys me. Life is worth living, and the human body such a perfect instrument that it hurts to see the thing wasted. Fundamentally I don't like intelligence. I have never been in love with an intellectual person. My friends seem generally to be intelligent, but I had much rather they were not: much rather that they didn't bump against things, and slide on carpets, and upset glasses, and open matchboxes upside down, and tumble over.

The trouble is that they don't do enough things with their bodies. My communist will have to fish. It will save his soul, during his own lifetime, to tie blood knots and evade cracking off his flies.

How safe would Karl Marx have been, I wonder, walking in a line of guns. Would he have mooned along star-gazing, and left a loaded gun against the wall at lunch, and shot his own foot off climbing over a stile? It is useless to retort with the obvious query about my average sports-man's usefulness in economics. Marx would have done these things, and been less efficient in consequence. I don't mind a great man being a communist, so long as he is a great man. And a great man is a man, and a man has a body, which is made to work. It is the physical inefficiency, the mechanic's gaucherie of an industrial age which does things with a lever instead of with the body, that disgusts me. It is the same with artists. You get the self-supposed genius, who never cleans his palette nor his brushes: for whom such practical considerations would be a sacrilege. The real genius, you find, uses not only turpentine, but soap and water. He can stretch his own canvas, knows which woods will warp, is a practised carpenter, and can light a fire. He does not grow in his head only, and get overbalanced by it, and tumble down. He remembers to take out his cartridges, relishes his blood knot, lives on true terms with the pleasures of his own body.

5. *x. xxxiv.*

What a lot of joy the people miss who can't live in the country. The urban chiel hates rain and cold, in fact every-thing except the vacuous sun—whose beams, at the climacteric, can just warm the rusty piston-metals of his heart. Not so the countryman, to whom the phenomena of nature are always interesting and (in England) generally useful. Hail, snow, ice, a rough wind: he remarks upon their depth or intensity every day. And to the lucky people winter means hunting, east winds duck, even the snow perhaps a spring salmon. There was never greater nonsense than the townsman's looking forward to the buds of spring. All seasons are beautiful. The wickedest people in the world are the smelly dowagers, stinking of chypre and synthetic pearls, who go to the Riviera in the winter, saying: 'You know, I must follow the sun.'

6. x. xxxiv.

And people little understand the country: even, alas, the countrymen. How many people can distinguish birds by their note? Lord Grey could do it, who must have had a musical ear; I, who have not, spend hours trying to work them out. The late spring is the time for this, as the earliest spring is the time for distinguishing trees. Trees are lovely things, and it is better to learn about them without leaves, because then your knowledge is fundamental. I used to hate them in Sussex, because I suspected them of stealing something out of the air. There were so many. There are too many in the Shire also, too many for them to enjoy an isolated individual royalty as in Gloucestershire; but they atone by making it easier to find a variety in a walk.

As soon as one begins to be good at a thing one begins to enjoy it. Trees, for me, used to be oaks, elms and beeches—wrongly diagnosed. Now that I know a little about them—not as a forester—I find them not only a fascinating occupation for the detective sense, but also more beautiful the better I know them. They have a refreshing tendency to break their own laws. You decide that a sycamore has certain characteristics, and then you find a sycamore that has none of them at all. You look at a tree for five minutes, not with the vacuous 'artistic' stare, but with concentration: looking to see if it is alternate or opposite, how the bark goes, what sort of buds it has, the general shape of its branches. You are alert for certain obvious peculiarities, which will make you say at once: 'Oh, this is a hemlock.' You are allowed to do a few quite fascinating experiments, such as pulling a needle off a spruce to see whether a bit of wood comes away with it. When you have made up your mind, you step back from an acquaintance, not from a stranger: a person whom you can appreciate with knowledge, and recognise afterwards at a distance, and wave to as you pass. It is at this stage that you suddenly appreciate its real beauty, the queer uncharacteristic way it turns over above its roots, or the brilliant symmetry with which it has arranged its branches.

I could put all I know about trees into three pages, and much of this knowledge would be wrong, all unacademic.* It would be worth doing, if one could send even one person out into a park, with the book. Find a park, in the early spring, before the leaf is on and play these games with it.

Everybody knows what a Xmas tree looks like, anything that remotely resembles a Xmas tree is called by most people a 'Fir.' There are two main kinds of this tree: the Fir and the Pine. The little soft spikes sticking out of a Fir tree go like a flat centipede, thus:

The sharper spikes of a Pine tree explode in bunches, thus: If it is a centipede and has a silvery trunk, it may be a *Silver Fir*. If it has little globules, like blisters down its reddish trunk, it may be a *Douglas Fir*. But in any case pop these blisters, which will exude a fir-smelling resin, and smear it on your hair. It

---

*I showed the following pages to an expert on trees, who nearly had a fit. It seems that there are things called ABIES and CUPRESSUS, and that my divisions are all wrong. Never mind: they work with me.

is very gummy, and will probably do irreparable damage, but at least it will be a change from synthetic brilliantine. If you have a moustache, put some on that. You will be able to sniff it all day. The next fir tree is a *Spruce*. Everything on this is inclined to droop. But the best test is to pull off one of the millepede legs, and if a tiny flinder of wood comes away with it, then it is what you thought. The legs are supposed to have four sides, instead of being quite flat; but as most self-respecting spruces decide to violate this law (to an unscientific eye) it seems best to place little reliance upon it. The *Yew*, which as every one knows is poisonous to horses, is darker than a spruce, has a distinctive red wood trunk, a flaky bark, and fleshy needles. The red trunk is the thing, amongst the dark foliage. A *Larch* is a conifer which sheds its leaves. A tree with cones but not foliage, which has a generally depressed and trailing appearance, is a larch. A *Sequoia* is great fun, for its bark is of about the same consistency as thick wads of blotting paper. It can be punched with the closed fist, quite hard, without discomfort. As it looks exactly like the bark of any other tree, this trick can be effectively performed before one's fiancée; but make sure it is a sequoia. A *Hemlock* is rather like a yew or a spruce, only it is covered with tiny cones.

If the tree is not a centipede-fir, but an exploding pine, then it may be a *Scottish Fir* (so named in order to confuse) which has branches all the way up. If its branches only begin towards the top, then it may be a normal *Pine*. If so, pull off a bit of the bark, and you will find it is fitted together inside itself in a jig-sawish kind of way. If the little bunches of explosives are each at the end of a knotty stalk, then it may be a *Cedar*. The cedar of Lebanon has shorter stalks and pines than the ordinary variety.

The conifers are quite enough for one day.

7. x. xxxiv.

The trees that are not coniferous (which I think the last lot were) are probably called deciduous. They also divide into two classes: Alternate and Opposite. An alternate tree is alleged to grow   its twigs alternately along the branches, thus: An opposite tree is alleged to grow its twigs sym- metrically, thus: It will be found that almost no tree does any- thing of the sort, most of them being a mixture   of the two, but a practised eye claims to be able to tell the difference.

Alternate trees include the *Beech*. Everybody knows what a beech looks like: it looks like a smooth elephant. They also include the lime, the elm, the holly, the Spanish chestnut, the poplar, the oak, the plane and the fruit trees. The *Lime* is an easy tree to recognise, for it has two peculiarities. It grows thick bunches of twigs out of itself just where it leaves the ground (sometimes also higher up), and it has a tendency to split its trousers. Where the bough leaves the trunk there is usually an inverted split in the fairly smooth bark. *Elms* have not got smooth bark: their twigs are inclined to be corky and knotty, like the back of a crocodile, and they are by no means the only other tree beside an oak. *Holly* is well known, except that it does not have to have spikes. There is a smooth-leaved variety, which must occasion an amount of dissatisfaction amongst urban purchasers at Xmas time. The edible or *Spanish Chestnut* (so called because it grows in Corsica or Sicily) has a remarkable bark: a rope-like, fluted trunk, deeply indented between the ridges, like the curling pelt of a dragon. *Poplar* has a trunk of modernistic texture, as if ornamented with hieroglyphics. *Plane* trees have bobbles, and the bark sometimes flakes off. *Oak* trees have buds in bunches at the end of the twig, and fortunately a good many of last year's dead leaves, with their characteristic shape, continue to adhere until the next lot comes: thus making it easier to identify a not very easy tree.

Opposite trees include the maple, the sycamore, and the ash. If I find an opposite tree that is neither a sycamore nor an ash, I say it is a *Maple*; but no doubt there is an easier way. A *Sycamore* has a trunk which looks as if it had been laid on heavily by an oil painter who might have called himself modern under King Edward. When young, the paint is smooth; when old, it begins to crack. It often looks like a beech, when young, but the great thing is that it is opposite. An *Ash* has little black buds and a characteristic tuft at the end of some of its twigs, a tuft of hanging flinders like thin dry grass, or osprey hat ornaments, or feathers. The *Horse Chestnut* has big sticky buds.

I have thought of two more alternate trees: the horn-beam and the gean. The *Hornbeam* has knobs on its branches, catkins, and a fluted or zigzag appearance if you look along its branches. The *Gean* or wild cherry has horizontal rings on its reddish bark, and when the bark splits these curl up like the tails of little pigs.

There also are *Helm Oak*, which reminds me of an olive tree, and the *Acacia*, which always looks like a dead chinese dragon; but I can't remember whether they are alternate or not.

If none of these will do, say it is an *Elder*.

8. x. xxxiv.

Another thing which my communist would be made to do would be to stay at home. He would be encouraged, in his green youth, to stay for a year on end upon the Continent, where he could upset his tummy with foreign foods (the stomach is really the basis of nationalism, it extends an umbilical to its native soil), ruin his happiness by neglecting his morals, on the principle that it doesn't matter what you do among foreigners, and get sick to death of the picturesque. Then he should come home.

Fortunately I worked the Continent out of my system, not in snippets, but in a lump. I know there is far more to see in Britain, far more beauty and interest, than can be crammed into seventy years. For to see Britain is not to motor through it. One has to work on a schedule for at least three years. In order to lay the foundations of one's country, one must go east for two months one year, north for two months the next, west for two months, and south. The two months must be spent in the same spot, without a car. I went to Norfolk the first time, and there stayed in a farmhouse within a furlong of the village pub for eight weeks. At the end of that time I had increased my weight by two stone, which gave some trouble in the hunting season, but I could say Yiss and Noo. I know something about Norfolk, far more than if I had driven up and down in it, because I have friends of Norfolk blood. When I have laid the four corners of my foundation I shall fill in the N.E. and S.W., the N.W., and the S.E., perhaps with only a month in each. Then there is the centre. One must keep a map and circle it. After twenty years one will have completed the preliminary investigation: one will know, more or less, which half-dozen counties twined most faithfully about the heart. One may even have a series of alternatives, to match the moods of the spirit: sleep in the east, fire in the west. There will be the opportunity of return. At sixty one will be able to go back: but not aimlessly, not fortuitously like an exhausted civil servant coming back sucked dry from Borneo and only too glad to settle anywhere. One will retire to the gem of the English world: where sport is inexhaustibly ready to wrap one from the world, where architecture is indigenous and interiors snug. At sixty one may be dreaming of the marches on the top of Ludlow Castle, or playing dominoes in the Nelson Arms, or hugging oneself in Coln St. Aldwyns; or jumping for joy in a Scottish castle, which any but a pig's heart would whinny to think of.

9. x. xxxiv.

This has been a queer week. On the 5th I had a day over my own with nine guns. The first and best drive of the morning was wrecked by Luke Fieldfare, whom I had left to direct the walkers whilst I placed the guns. He had arrived ¾ of an hour late to begin with: bless him. Unfortunately I introduced him to Mrs Ransome before giving him his instructions, and this went to his head, so that he did not listen.

'Do you hear, Luke? I want them driven towards the house.'

'Yes, old boy. Yes, Mrs. Ransome. Sit down, Timmie!'

'You know: the way we did it before.'

'Yes, Mrs. Ransome. Yes, old boy. Timmie, sit!'

'You do understand, don't you?'

'Sit down, will you. Yes. Yes, Mrs. Ransome, of course.'

The result was that he drove the roots parallel to the guns instead of towards them. All the birds went across us, and I was as rude as I could be to him, in front of everybody. More strained relations.

The next thing was that as soon as we had reached a critical field, with forty or fifty out-manoeuvred birds before us, we would find a decrepit old labourer in the middle of it, gathering mushrooms, and not a bird to be seen. This happened twice. From Wilson's, Tilly's, Brown's and Higgins' we only got a brace.

Then a difficult lunch. Then, in my best drive of the day at Bourne's, Luke, Fred and another breasted a ridge above the kale, arm in arm and talking loudly, whilst they were taking position for the drive. The two main coveys, of 18 and 21, left at once. I had warned them of this before, and fairly lost my temper—offering command to Luke and refusing to take any more responsibility myself. There was nothing left for this drive except a couple of coveys at the beaters' end, and these they succeeded in letting out, by keeping their left well back. So it went on. We could get nothing out of the wood—though this was expected—and the day ended with about two brace, three hares and a few rabbits or pigeons.

I went out next day with a boy to help walk, and shot a brace in Wilson's—left and right. I also missed a hare.

On the 8th I went out again with the boy, and missed a cock pheasant both barrels.

On 9th I went out again with a boy, and killed a brace at Bourne's—left and right. I missed a rabbit, and hit a hare in the quarters with No. 6 shot at a long range. Any decent person would give up shooting so far.

The old mushroomer who spoils manoeuvres only worries one at the time. He is an interesting person really. His price varies so greatly with the progress of his season that the cost of mushrooms is as good a calendar to the passage of autumn as my dandelion clock used to be, when I was a little boy, to the passage of the day. When the regular mushroom harvest is over he gathers Blue Stalks, which are equally edible; and he himself eats his captures *raw*, and will not eat them at all if they have grown under the shadow of an oak.

10. x. xxxiv.

The trouble about the intellectual is that he misses a lot of fun: as himself would be the first to admit. But he oughtn't to admit it. He ought to do something about it. If a man was an admirable specimen he wouldn't lag behind in certain directions. If Newton was absent-minded so much the worse for him, just as much as it was the worse for Beethoven to be deaf. A happy man, and this I take it is what all men wish to be and might be if they could avoid distortion, is a man who has advanced in a balanced way. Intelligence is based upon logic, and the tools of logic are merely nouns and verbs—a formal distinction which seems to have little support nowadays. The static noun and the active verb correspond to the other exploded dualities: space and time, matter and mind. Logic is bound to lose its predominance, will rightly lose it, as mind and matter coalesce into formal aspects of something else, as space and time are recognised to be inseparable, and as the verb-plus-noun language yields to a symbolism based upon Bergson's 'becoming'—a question, perhaps, of verbs, participles and adverbs. If this is so, it seems to me that logic and hence what we have always called 'intellect' are facets of reality not necessarily dependable or always advantageous. This might account for some quite 'stupid' people being obviously more successful livers than the intelligensia. It might mean that in some other suppressed faculty lies the better decision. In fact, that the epicurean was a better philosopher than the stoic.

But whatever the deeper meanings may be, certainly it is useless to rely on the intelligence only. The desirable specimen is the specimen, I take it, whose physical and emotional efficiency is at least on a par with that of his intelligence.

And it is a curious fact that people who have developed exclusively in one direction, instead of along all three, generally tend to be unacceptable to the rest of their race: either as semi-anthropoid Rugby internationals swinging themselves along on their knuckles, or melodramatic actresses (too much emotion) or communists slouching about with tremendous self-sacrifice, doubtless, but an unpleasant sense of intellectual grievance, and less good humour than can be discovered in a porcupine.

11. x. xxxiv.

Yesterday John Dulden, self and the sergeant lay for the duck on the octagon, but they didn't come in. I went on the island for the first time. It is the best place.

To-day Tom Bourne rang up at 2 o'clock and said he was going out for rabbits round the hedgerows with a friend: would I care to come? I went till 4 o'clock. We had 3 rabbits, 1 leveret and 2 partridges. I was on my day, for of these I had all but one rabbit. There was a possibility that I had another bird which towered but was not picked. They are going to look for it this evening. If found this will make my 3rd consecutive left and right on partridges, which is not bad for a feeble shot, under varied conditions.

12. *x. xxxiv.*

Slew one Frenchman. The pleasures of this part of the year, between the start of the shooting season and the first hunt, are of a confused nature in the Shire: because two things are going on at once. I may be cubbing with the Warden on the same morning as I am shooting with Luke. There is a kind of composite pleasure. The basis of autumnal feeling is early rising, because of cub hunting and the rare stubble-feeding duck.

Good and great men have unanimously insisted on the necessity of early rising. Cobbett would have placed it just above going to church and just below marrying a wife who could do housework in the snow. I don't know whether Cobbett found it as difficult to get up as I do, but if he did, he would have insisted on it all the more. When I go to bed on the night before cubbing, I do so without the least certainty that I shall get up. So when I do get up it is an achievement, a matter of satisfaction for hours. All achievements are satisfactory, and mine, a sort of diurnal raising of Lazarus from the dead, atones for its inconveniences. I find that I can usually wake up for shooting or cubbing without a watch. Indeed, if you are living in the country it is good to do without a watch altogether. It keeps you alert, gives you a more vital position in the cycle of the day, and in an emergency you can always ask.

The pleasure of cubbing is largely that of getting up in time to do it: but it is also pleasant to get another glimpse of a scarlet coat, and to see an excited tinker yelling like a demon at a cub which is charging him face to face, and to stray off eating hazel nuts, and to slay a Frenchman, feeling hardy, the same afternoon.

13. x. xxxiv.

Luke Fieldfare's. We had seven guns, and slew five brace, four hares. I had a brace, and a hare. They were high, swinging birds: everybody missing. Made it up with Luke, who was as nice as could be. It was a happy day.

They were cubbing in Three Woods this morning, and saw neither foxes nor pheasants.

The pleasures of shooting in the Shire really depend upon the unimportance of the sport. In evading all extremes, we have evaded being a shooting county. A few, very few, great houses preserve their game; but apart from that we are not fanatical. There is little to be satisfied with, and so we have to be satisfied with little. This is pleasant.

The sportsman is happy out of doors even without his gun, or without using it. One day last spring I was walking round Three Woods, to keep down the young rabbits. I came out of the wood stealthily, and there were two pairs of pheasants. The further pair saw me first, because they were outside the long grass, and made for safety in the characteristic pheasant way. That is to say, the hen flew and the cock ran. Cocks are cowardly, I suppose because nature does not have to manufacture the male to withstand pain, as she does the female. Then the nearer pair saw me, and the hen flew at once; but the cock squatted. His head shot up vertically out of the grass when he noticed me, and vanished instantly with the same sort of motion. I thought: 'Very well, you crafty old devil, I shall give you a fright.' I began to walk up towards him, anticipating with pleasure the terrific leap of agitation with which he would leave the ground if I could get up close. But suddenly, before I had come within thirty yards of him, there were a hare's ears in front of me in the long grass. She seemed to be feeding quite unconsciously, and the big furry concavities, like ship's ventilators, turned this way and that. I went slowly to within a couple of yards without disturbing her, but the moment I stopped she was off. Her ears went flat, she puffed out her body as if she were taking a great quavering breath, she nerved herself to the effort, and then she was bounding away. Her hind legs lifted her behind. They are longer than the forelegs, and this, I believe, makes hares run faster uphill. I put up the pheasant afterwards, but somehow he was not important after puss. She faced me dead on, as she was taking her breath, and so I could see the two eyes set square back on the sides of the head: eyes which seem not to see very well forwards, so that hares sometimes blunder into you if you are directly in front. I had approached her from dead ahead, and perhaps this is why I got so close. I have remembered her for six months, and now write her down, thinking of the bright salmon-pink blood on the hare's cleft nostrils that I harled and slung over the hasp of a gate at Luke Fieldfare's, six months later.

15. x. xxxiv.

My next novel must be picaresque. A pursuit perhaps, with Russian spies, a great-great-grandson of William Wordsworth, aeroplanes, and a drunk wildfowler lying in a puddle with two bottles of whisky. Also a Harem out for a walk, in a crocodile; and the suggestion of a local anaesthetic for boys who have got to be beaten at school.

16. x. xxxiv.

Pubs shall wean my communist from his cross. Not the kind that appears in the illustrated weeklies under the title 'Mine Ease at Mine Inn,' not the famous and the bogus, and not necessarily the comfortable. Merely the grubby

little tied houses for farm labourers, which have to fight to
pay their way. The pub is the club, in which the real people
consort for friendship. There are no kinder people, and no
better tempered people, than the inhabitants of the
Crown. They are never drunk, and they would not mind if
they were. They go for love and comfort, and they get it.
You can do anything in a pub, except be mean.

One of the things about the public-house recently has
been the arty fashion for it. The mechanics and fund-
holders stream out from the Wen, sometimes screaming
and giggling and condescending, always at heart uncomfortable. It takes six months in the same pub to evict
condescension without condescending. It takes the same
time to learn darts and to appreciate beer. The people in the
Crown are there for direct reasons: they want a little love,
three pints of hops. To pass the time away, and as an
excuse for the beer (for there is half a pint betted on every
game) they play darts, or nap (if tired), or crib, or tipit, or
shove-penny. They play these games with the same
interest and attention as the Wen-man plays his billiards,
but with warmer hearts. Darts is a good and difficult
game, not a light-opera country pastime like dancing
round the maypole.

The presence of a so-called gentleman alters the centre
of gravity of the pub. The rustic closes his mouth, sarcastically becomes the bumpkin which he is supposed to
be. Not sarcastically, for that conveys an idea of bitterness
which is not present, but with an eye that misses nothing.
If the gentleman is really a gentleman he is still going to
have a lot of difficulty. The social system conditions the
system against him with its weight. I think I may truly say
that every person of my own age in Tenmere uses my
Christian name, whilst my elders give me the prefix 'Mr.'
because I give it to them. I have not expressed the wish. It
has taken a year to get there. The reason must be that like
Mr. Salteena I am not quite a gentleman.

17. x. xxxiv.

If one could whip up the faintest conviction that by being killed in a war one was being killed for England, it would be worth doing. I should like to have a country course for politicians, in which they would learn to set their rabbit wires a hand-breadth high, and for hares a thumb higher.

19. x. xxxiv.

One partridge, one barrel (nearly shooting Ker) and about five barrels at a climbing squirrel. They are having a correspondence in the weekly papers about the most difficult shot. It is the squirrel on the zig-zag branch: say of a hornbeam.

20. x. xxxiv.

One partridge, two barrels. The best of my poor shoot is that it can only stand two public days. After that it is a question of going round by oneself, or of taking one or two companions for an hour or two, on the distinct understanding that it is only for a walk. And these lonely stalks are interesting. You get to know the coveys and the habits of the birds and the moods of the fields themselves. There was a covey of thirty frenchmen on Three Woods at the beginning of the season, but they have vanished. It is as strange as the mystery of the *Waratah*.

22. x. xxxiv.

I missed both barrels at a long covey. Tom Bourne's was swarming with birds in odd places, perhaps the result of beagling. Witherby's beagles were there on Saturday, ran into a fox in Three Woods and vanished from human ken. However much Bourne's may swarm, it is difficult to get birds because of the bigness of the fields. What it really needs is about 40 guns to line every hedge, and content to get only about one bird each. Also 40 beaters, which would be ridiculous for the percentage of game.

To-night there was a magnificent full moon. I went to try the duck, but they didn't oblige—except one flight. Wings in the air, streaks across the powdered trees, once, twice, then half a dozen splashes. I fired instantly at the back splashes (I ought to have chosen the front ones, or, better, not have fired at all) and again at the white streaks when they got up. It was far across. The second barrel was certainly ineffective, but I shall see to-morrow whether the first did anything.

A most curious phenomenon to-night. I was standing motionless, looking N.N.E. There was a big flash (as big as one or two finger-breadths at the stretch of my arm) like lighting a few millimetres of magnesium wire behind the (cirrus) clouds. It was not the colour of magnesium— more that of gun-cotton, as if an observation balloon at 40 or 50,000 feet had suddenly blown up. It went silently. Puff! like that. It did not drop like a shooting star, but just as lit magnesium *appears* to drop. Elevation about 25 degrees. It made me flinch.

23. x. xxxiv.

I went alone to Bourne's, and missed two rabbits. Along with the advantage of having an unimportant shoot, there is the advantage of being an unimportant shot. I can't believe one would enjoy one's kills very much without a nice percentage of misses.

I tore my trousers climbing over barbed wire. Jefferies has a fine reflection on the unfriendliness of this kind of fencing. Not only does it callously ruin hunting, but also goes to the extreme churlishness of being *unsituponable*.

24. x. xxxiv.

I went round the same places with Tom Bourne, taking his terrier Pip and two sheepdogs. Tom shot two rabbits. I missed three rabbits and killed a cock pheasant. So my shots at ground game have gone to rack and ruin, again, just when I thought I was getting into practice. In the dust I fired at least ten cartridges at a bat, and finally winged him. They were No. 4's. I shall use 4's and 5's for the rest of the season, as an experiment. No shots at partridges, though we saw plenty. They are wild as hawks.

27. x. xxxiv.

Ker, Allweather, Tom Bourne, self, Cobb and three ferrets, on a blusterous day. Nothing liked bolting. The ditches were overgrown and difficult to shoot. We had four rabbits, one hare, one pigeon, one partridge. I was shooting much better at them, with left arm fully extended. I drove the partridges over, three coveys, beautifully high.

But it is the ferreting that was the important thing to-day. Rabbits hate bolting in a wind, but we had fixed to meet beforehand and so we didn't call it off. It was nice to see the uncertain yellow faces again, turning this way and that at the mouth of a bury. Their red eyes blink vaguely at the waiting guns. They snuffle along outside the caverns, or turn back into them with a look of resignation. They hasten slowly. It is as if their long subjugation to man, their confinement generally in rather insanitary little boxes, had made them forget about the open air. Aimlessly, forgetfully, prisoners on ticket-of-leave, no longer quick like a weasel, they cock short-sighted heads and stare at you. They turn and loom back into the hole. The head goes, the back presents itself, the tail vanishes with a little quiver.

I got more interested in them than the shooting, and

generally volunteered to stay when one of them laid up. We muzzle our ferrets with string, behind the tusks and under and over the jaws: in Sussex we used to line them. We tried a bell on the collar, so that you could tell where the ferret was. When a ferret does lay up you are supposed to gut a rabbit at the mouth of the bury, and the smell brings the ferret out. Unfortunately, in my case it has never done so. A far better way is to fire a gun down the mouth of the hole. The noise inside must be prodigious, and the ferret generally pops out immediately afterwards shaking its head and saying 'What the hell was that?'

28. x. xxxiv.

I had a beautiful opportunity yesterday for shewing off to Cobb and Ker. They came over the brow of the hill without my noticing them, just as I had spotted a rabbit crouching well out in the field. I walked up to within about fifteen yards of the rabbit, waved my leg at it in a mock kick to make it run, gave it a little law, and bowled it over neatly first barrel. Ker applauded, and I looked up with a flush of pleasure that this singular piece of magnanimity and skill had been observed.

29. x. xxxiv.

I killed one pigeon, using John Dulden's lovely Westley Richards, as on Saturday, but never saw a bird. I can't describe the drive and accuracy of this gun. You feel the shot go from the shoulder and keep together all the way to the bird, as if there was an invisible but tangible line linking you to it. With my gun there is just a bang and a fortuitous death—not a venomous arm reaching through the air for its prey.

1 . xi . xxxiv .

To-day, more than thirteen hundred years ago, the patron saint of Shireham was born. His name was St. Rumbold. On the day of his birth he announced his adherence to the Christian faith, on the next day he gave directions for his funeral and interment, and on the third day, exhausted by these early labours, he expired. Thirteen centuries later, I toasted him to-night with some libations.

3 . xi . xxxiv .

For several days now the weather has been frosty and I have been lurking about the lakes for duck. Desultory shooting has yielded two rabbits on Bourne's. On Friday I shot round Frank Derby's at Clive, and we killed a brace of partridges and one rabbit between us. I had one partridge, and missed two easy shots at the very end. But the duck are the interesting things.

They began to come with the frost, but it has been cunning work trying to get up to them (once on the water) and they have been coming in *after* dusk, when shooting has been impossible. On Friday I saw four mallard, three pochard, three tufted and a greater crested grebe. I managed to catch the mallard in the reeds, far off, and knocked down the leader by taking the choke barrel first. But he was only hard hit. He fell at an angle of about 30 degrees, instead of tail over tip, recovered in about forty seconds, and swam slowly off. I spent half an hour trying to get near him, knowing all the time that I ought to be at Derby's, and then had to give him up. On Saturday there were only the mallard and the tufted and the grebe. I put Ker by the reeds, and, going round to the bathing enclosure, fired a shot into the tufted at harmless range to put them over him. But he had posted himself in full view. They got up and flew between us. They wheeled towards

me. Like a fool I tried to replace the used cartridge before
they arrived. They came over beautifully, low and swinging; but like Achilles I was arming, weeping, cursing,
vowing vengeance. They were past before I had shut the
gun. I had a miss-pull with the safety catch on as usual.
Then, with the catch off at last, I missed a long barrel.
Curses not loud, but deep. The tufted, however, were
silly. They kept swinging round the lake, wondering what
we were, getting higher and higher. On the second circuit
they came within long range, and I hit the leader, breaking
his leg. He took two more circuits and landed, to find that
he was unable to get up again. We spent an hour shooting
at him from the banks, and chasing him in a canoe, whilst
he dived. Cobb managed to upset the canoe and fall in: a
clumsy, slow-motion immersion. Finally this duck also
disappeared and we went off to Tom Bourne's for rabbits.
All the time the grebe had been swimming about
nervously, watching us and wondering. I yelled to Ker,
telling him not to shoot it.

At half-past six, in the dark, Laddie shouted in at my
window that a grebe (believed to be) had been found half
dead outside, and would I bring a gun to kill it. I said I
would not bring a gun, and would kill it if necessary.
There was a group of half a dozen boys, and Andrew with
a torch. He said: 'You shooters are rotten shots, shooting
grebes.' I said: 'It has nothing whatever to do with me, and
if you say that again I will knock you down.' They had by
now lost the bird in question. After a bit of searching, they
gave it up and went indoors, but I was not going to be left
under the imputation of shooting grebes. I borrowed the
torch and stayed with Laddie. We found him quite
quickly, as soon as we had found out where he was first
and last seen, and in what direction he was going. He was
reported as being a black bird with white underneath, and
a tuft, waddling in a pool of blood and scarcely able to
move. Of course I diagnosed him as the wounded tufted,
but everybody swore that he definitely had a pointed beak.

Anyway, we found him. There he sat in the double pool of electric light, and he was a greater crested grebe.

I made Laddie hold the light on him to dazzle or hypnotise him, walked round behind, and dropped my coat across him gently. Then I took hold of his beak through my coat and carefully worked him out. When he was clear we looked at him. His wings were sound. His head and neck were sound. There was no blood on his breast. The only blood was on one of his curious half-webbed toes, faintly reminiscent of squashed bananas, and even more arresting, when we saw them, than his beak and demon's head. It was a mere abrasion, the skin hardly broken.

I took him to show Charles and Peter. In the strong electric light we looked over him again and he was as sound as a bell. Then we carried him carefully down to the lake, in a cold night conscious of my shirt sleeves, whilst he hissed and grated. We looked him over and over once more, to see if he was old or young, and found grey at the top of his feathers. He was plump. I held him by the beak and lowered him gently into the water, that you couldn't see the surface of, under the torch. When his legs broke the surface you could see it was there, grey, limpid, clear, cold. I let go of his beak and took my hand away quickly, but he was gone quicker still. He dived like a conjuring trick and was out of the torch's light. In a few seconds he popped out again with a loud noise, some way off; but we never saw him again.

On going back over the terrain, we found the rumoured pool of blood. There were two tiny spots, which would correspond to the two steps of his left foot, on the gravel.

He had simply been a bewildered water animal, clumsy on land, who had cut his foot. Now, did he walk all the way up from the lake (¼ mile) and, if so, why? or did he pitch on the gravel for some unknown reason, and cut his foot in doing so, or hit a telephone wire? or what?

On Sunday morning I couldn't spot him, but I only had a few minutes to look. What fun if he stayed!

5. xi. xxxiv.

Guy Fawkes Day. Up at 6 o'clock and got to the lake for an indeterminate dawn. The three tufted (if it was the same three, then the fellow I gave up on Saturday must have recovered) were on the octagon, on my side. I had been trying to get a duck for Laddie so long, and was so enraged at the two losses of last week, that my morale gave way, and I sent them the choke barrel on the water. For one thing, it was the only way of making them get up and go over Lizzie. But it was blood-lust that did it: quite pure, unreasoning, unsporting. Blake would have approved. It knocked two of them silly. I went for the punt. The third went over Lizzie and vanished. When I was just coming out of the boat-house, one of my two came to its senses and flew away, a tough specimen. I picked one dead bird.

Till eight o'clock I made manoeuvres round the Oxford Water and Copper Bottom, trying to drive things to Lizzie.

On our way there we found the spare tufted on the Eleven Acre. I put Lizzie on the high dive and gave it the cylinder at 80 yards from the reeds at the other side to move it. It went over him beautifully and he missed both barrels.

I killed a sitting rabbit, or practically sitting. He just unsat.

As we went back to breakfast I saw the grebe. There she swam, a puzzled Khaki Z, as large as life and perfectly happy. So much (a) for shooting grebes, and (b) for scaring them away by shooting over them.*

Immediately after breakfast we went up to the home

*She nested here the following spring.

field. Tommy Roberts shot his pheasants at Roof House on Saturday, so there were hopes. They were fulfilled. We saw four hen pheasants and a cock running into the bracken as we arrived. I hurried round to the Roof House fence and left Lizzie to walk them up, assuming that he might get the first shot and I the second, as they came for Roof House, if he missed. But we could put nothing up. Our hen broke at last, well away to my left. I fired the choke first, and must have missed, for she looked in range. I then gave her a hopeless cylinder, out of temper. She went on her way rejoicing.

We kept at it, beating bushes and wandering about. At last I spotted the cock, making a dash from a bush, and ran like a lunatic to put him back. Succeeded. I sent Lizzie to the bush and he put him out rather clumsily, missing both barrels.

In the afternoon we made a round tour, partly thwarted by rain, labourers in stubble fields, and Wetherby's beagles, so that we couldn't get up to anything; except a silly hare, who came loping towards me, end on, at half a mile an hour, and was duly slain.

I also missed a snipe, with No. 4 shot, and felt perfectly certain that I had killed him dead: a characteristic of snipe, I suppose.

6. xi. xxxiv.

Up at 5.45 and down to the lake in the night darkness, but we did not get a shot. The grebe was there. Five mallard came in from the west. The wind is N.E. so there may be hopes on Wednesday evening. Then to the borders of Roof House, and slew yesterday's hen pheasant. She seemed Mongolian or Chinese. Saw no others.

My last was a poor book. The next will be a better one, but lacking in one particular. It does not appreciate the winter, or not half enough. I suppose this is a natural result of having been written in the summer. Winter: darkness, cold, increase of the senses of touch and smell: comfort after exhaustion: sensations heightened. Northern man, with something to bite on.

The low-down on sitting shots: My duck, rabbit and hare yesterday not only gave me no pleasure, but also made me feel miserable for them. I felt that I had murdered a live thing. To-day's pheasant, who was crossed off neatly, first barrel, on the wing, did not inspire any feelings of pity at all. It was not a live thing murdered, but a good shot. One is a concrete assassination of beauty, the other is a creation of beauty—the beautiful aim.

Shooting sitting is not unsporting, but unsatisfactory. It produces no elation and so leaves time for remorse to breed. No art has compensated the destruction which one is left to contemplate. A mere dead hare: horrible. But a hare cut over so that he somersaults with his head on the ground: beauty.

There be some sports are painful, and their labour
Delight in them sets off.

THE TEMPEST

7. xi. xxxiv.

Killing is beginning to become clear to me. It came as an inspiration. Before, I had been puzzled at liking to kill things, because I am generally more humane than most people: certainly than the warmongers, the flogging magistrates, the snake killers, and most schoolmasters. I cannot remember when I last killed a fly, or a wasp, or a mouse. It is, as I discovered yesterday, a question of art. When it is difficult to kill the thing, when skill and achievement come into it, I find that the killing is worth while. You forget the dead salmon in the ecstasy of creation: you have perfected something yourself, even more perfect than the dead fish. This must sound silly to anybody who has not shared the perfection; who has not created a cast, or a shot, or a run, himself. But it is rock bottom.

To triumph over difficulties is the essence of sportsmanship. This is what the dear old colonels mean, the colonels whose apparent brain weight would give the common vole a sensation of volatility in his head, when they talk about the 'sporting chance.' Such-and-such a sport, they say, is not a decent one, because the such-and-such doesn't get a 'sporting chance.' They are absolutely right. They mean that the sport is not sufficiently difficult to make the kill worth while. The pleasure of surmounting the difficulty is not enough to counteract the displeasure of killing a beautiful thing.

This is why I stopped fishing on the 24th of April. It was worth killing the silver superlative of a salmon when it took a day to do it: three in one day lowered the achievement, so I stopped. It was becoming a slaughter, not a sport.

This, also, is why the Englishman kills his trout with a dry fly and imposes a limit. Robin, who is a Canadian, told me an illuminating story which runs as follows: 'I was brought up in Canada, and used to fish there. After I left Sandhurst and got posted to my regiment, a major came into the mess and asked if there were any fishermen present who would like to fish with him to-morrow. I said that I knew all about it and would love to come. Actually I didn't know a dry fly from a wet one. I classed them all as flies. I go hot and cold when I think of that major and what I told him. But he was decent. He took me in hand and taught me real fishing. Then there was the war. Afterwards I went back to Canada, and fished again. But it was humiliating to find that, after all I had learnt, the three and four-pounders were breaking my gut, whilst the Canadian farmer who fished next to me with a telegraph pole and a cable was actually throwing them out backwards over his head.' The answer to Robin is, of course, that the farmer was merely fishing for the pot, as one might rear pigs, whilst Robin was practising an art. The rare fish of three pounds that did not break his 4X cast ('leader,' they call it) was an achievement beyond the farmer's. Anybody can catch a trout on a worm. If you use a worm, except for the pot-fishing, you have nothing to achieve and to congratulate yourself upon.

Hence the, to the foreigner, astonishing spectacle of an Englishman handicapping himself. I read in a book once that an Englishman even handicaps his drink. He puts brandy into his port, waits fifty years for the brandy to work itself out again, and then drinks it, in exactly the same state as it started, with reverence and exultation. In Canada, apparently, they kill salmon by the daily score. In England even, I was sorry to see that some woman or other has killed between sixteen and twenty in one day.★ That was not sport, not achievement over difficulty: it was butchery. It cannot have been difficult to raise those fish: a question merely of dolloping in the fly, and walking up ard down the bank for ten minutes, and gaffing the fish. Give her, at an underestimation, ten minutes per fish. She must have been actually playing the fish she killed for nearly three and a half hours of her day. If I know anything of the gentry, and she was a titled woman, she did not start before 10.30, nor fish after 6, and took at least an hour off for luncheon. This leaves her about six fishing hours, with fish on for more than half the time—provided that she really did kill her fish in ten minutes, a fact of which I am doubtful. Where is the difficulty, where the achievement, where the sport? I can't help feeling that I should have gone home after the first four.

This is why the stories of Canadian abundance leave me unmoved: why I can reasonably abominate snake-killers whilst myself killing partridges: why my heart moves for a dead mouse but exults over a dead pheasant in his pride. After all, there is a lot of blank air for the shot to go into, besides the pheasant.

8. xi. xxxiv.

I should like the people who kill bags of a thousand birds to have been with me to-day, and I wonder whether they would have enjoyed it. I was up at 5.45 and met Laddie

---

*Which is by no means a record. The best example I know, of this astonishingly stupid attitude towards sport, is that of Franz Ferdinand. His, however, was an achievement with the gun. He used to shoot at Konopišt with no less than seven weapons and four loaders, and he once killed more than 4,000 birds, himself, in one day. (*A propos* of statistics, and quite beside the point: a Yorkshireman once drank 52½ pints of beer in one hour.] Now why did Franz Ferdinand do this? Even if he shot for twelve hours at a stretch, without pause for luncheon, it means that he killed six birds in each minute of the day. The mere manual labour, a pheasant every ten seconds for twelve successive hours, is enough to make a road-mender stagger; and there is little wonder that, by the time the unhappy archduke had accumulated his collection of 300,000 head of game, he was shooting with rubber pads on his coat and a bandage round his ears. The unfortunate man had practically stunned himself with gunpowder, long before they bagged him also at Sarajevo.

between the lakes. It was a grand frosty morning, and as soon as the sun came, he came in red, tinting the thick hoar saffron, between the melted patches where the sheep had been lying down. It had been a duck's frost. The octagon was frozen, the Eleven Acre half. I sent Laddie with my gun, round the Eleven Acre in a wide circuit, with instructions to stand at the gap nearest the Boating Island. I took his four-ten. After giving him full eight minutes, and now it was light, I walked down the north bank, where I knew they would be. They were, and I sent two flights, of about eight each, exactly over the gap. He, however, had posted himself by the bathing shed. Not a shot.

I am interested in English literature, and I shoot, and yesterday I was thinking about synchronised crime. All these subjects hinge on the one factor: precise comprehension. In 70 per cent. of our conversations, and 99 per cent. of all literary appreciation, something goes wrong with the message, between mouth and ear. I say 'shakes hands with delectable odours' and am not understood to mean 'says good-bye to the sense of smell'; I say 'go to the gap next the boating island' and am understood to mean the bathing sheds; how on earth can a criminal rely upon his accomplice in smash and grab? No wonder they get caught. How can two ever be made one in the marriage service, when they can't even make themselves understood by one another? How can there be an entente between nations with separate tongues, if individuals, using the same language, might as well be Hottentot and Esquimaux? Man is unshakably alone.

We went up by the tennis courts and a rabbit ran into a bush. I shot into the bush, two feet in front of me, as he went in, and broke a back leg. You always seem to break the back legs of rabbits. This was my only barrel. Laddie, instead of shooting him as he crawled across the path, dithered and ran. He got away, to die horribly, I suppose.

By the tennis courts a cock pheasant announced his invincibility, quite close. I ran round his plantation, to the

Doric Bridge, leaving Laddie to come through from the Temple. But there he was, crouching like a domestic hen that wants to be mounted. His shoulders were high, his neck and tail well on the ground. I was torn between emotions. On the one hand a pheasant is a rarity to us, and a good thing to shew off; on the other hand, I get no pleasure from a sitting shot. But I only had the fourteen. Could I risk waiting till he flew? I aimed at him, like the most determined murderer, and fired. He got up with a tremendous start, leaving six body feathers (two cut in half) and flew straight at Laddie, not rising very much. Laddie missed him, and he vanished in the trees, where Laddie forgot to mark him down. So I have the satisfaction of knowing that (1) I have shot a sitting cock, (2) he is lying dead somewhere, without being any good to anybody. It is like murdering an old lady and then finding that she has pawned her jewels. We searched for 20 minutes, and gave it up. Among other things I know now that it will be lunacy to start next season without a good dog, however expensive.

The home field was blank, and I got back for breakfast at 8.

I worked till 12.30 and then went out again, with 3 sandwiches, Robin and two boys. It rained continuously till sunset. I missed one rabbit. Robin shot a weasel (locally called a wizzle). My efforts to drive a few coveys over him were frustrated by each of the boys in turn: one by shouting a loud question at the wrong moment, and the other by waving his arms. I walked the whole afternoon, trying to send things to Robin, in vain. The birds are now more cunning than carrion crows. At about 3.30 we thought it might be worth while to beat a bit of wood. Unfortunately Robin started off in the wrong direction, lost himself, and remained lost for nearly an hour. In one way this seems very funny, but it frightened me at the time. I had heard his gun go off, when he shot at a pheasant, and thought he must have killed himself. At dusk we got back on the car;

and ate sausage-rolls, bananas, and cheese sandwiches (with coffee) by the light of the roof lamp. It had been a completely blank day and we were soaked to the skin. I stayed in my bath (with Sloan's liniment in it) for an hour and a half reading *Dos Passos*.

9. xi. xxxiv.

Up at 5.45. But yesterday's red sun was right, and the afternoon's drizzle was still going on. It was muggy. Saddened by experience of Laddie, I decided to put myself in the proper gap and leave Ker and Robin to turn them to me if they could. At least I should get a shot as they came in. Of course they didn't come.

It seems a boring thing to record the time of getting up, on a blank day. But shooting of this sort, like fishing, is not boring even when it is blank. It is not only lovely to get up when everybody else is asleep: it is lovely merely to stand still while the sun rises, to be a part of all the bird calls and the rises of fish, to have one's gun weighing on one's arm, and, with the faculties all alert, to be *patient*, absorbed in a place and attitude.

The Warden has foot and mouth.

10. xi. xxxiv.

It must be five years since I broke my leg, and ever since then I have been afraid of hunting: on and off. This is odd. At intervals of about two years I fall in love and then I am not afraid of hunting any more. For that season I go well. Then I seem to have worked the poison out of me, realise that life is worth living and begin to go carefully again. It is difficult for a man with an imagination, who has broken something in a fall, to go well on a bad horse in the Duke's country. I mean a £70 horse, not up to one's weight. Anyway, fortunately, at the moment life doesn't matter two pins; and this is going to be a good season.

To-day is the first since March that I have put a leg across a horse. The end of last season didn't go in the diary, because I was sick of writing books about hunting and I couldn't be bothered; besides, I had filled my book and was too lazy to get another. But to-day we are off again. To-day, I have put on my long pants, for the first time this winter. To-day Silver, with a pot belly (I could only afford to get him up on the 1st November) looked keen, kind, beautiful: shied when Peter cracked his whip: jumped three fences and a brook—the fences perfectly. I rode Sparks on the way home. He is the lazy horse that used to belong to a clergyman. A crop and a pair of spurs may make him go—if his wind is right. He whistles a bit. But if it is right then I believe I can make him go with the Duke's, and keep Silver for the Warden. The latter was not up to weight, but less sluggish. High hopes, therefore, for the season.

11. xi. xxxiv.

The Shire dialect is a pleasant and interesting one, which can be reduced to a few easy rules, like English Grammar. The first rule is to omit the common or garden 'w' whilst supplying a few of your own. Thus a woman is an ooman, and your wife is your Wold ooman. The second, more curious, rule deals with the crushed past participle. For 'frozen' we say 'friz'; for 'frightened,' 'frit'; for 'written,' 'writ.' The man who has been warped by his education can only rise to the abbreviation 'isn't,' but we extend this throughout the verb 'to be.' 'Be'nt' is as good as 'isn't.' Thus, if I were asked for a short sentence illustrative of all that is best in the Shire, I should produce:

'A be'ant frit of my Wold ooman.'

17. xi. xxxiv.

One sitting hare, to spite the beagles.

But a hare is always very much appreciated in the Shire. It seems that the actual flesh value of the hare and the pheasant makes up for the cold-blooded murder. It does not make it satisfactory, but it just makes up for it.

18. xi. xxxiv.

I have had to sit down under such a lot of guff in definition of the 'gentleman,' from the pulpit, the maternal lecture and the pure-bred snob, that I really don't see why I shouldn't begin defining him myself. I define him by his hospitality. The infallible test for a gentleman is to drop in upon him suddenly at an awkward hour, preferably at half-past nine o'clock in the evening, unfed, and see what he does about it. If he is too mean to do anything but pass it off as a breach of good manners, or if he rings for the butler and provides you with a caviare sandwich or some such flummery, then he is no friend of ours. But if his wife dives into the kitchen, and provides you *there* with the best in the house, even if it is only *bread and butter* (though there is sure to be some little relish), at a moment's notice, and if the kitchen is clean, then that person is a gentleman and God is with his house.

Hunters shall go to heaven when they die, and live in this world more joyfully than any other men.

16TH CENTURY

23. xi. xxxiv.

The first hunting day of my third season with the Duke's.

I am afraid I'm not really so mad on hunting as it would be genteel to pretend. As my income dwindles I shall give up shooting first of all, then hunting, then flying, then fishing. But hunting is only a sort of makeshift for me. Perhaps, if one could afford to do it in a style to which the country is accustomed, hunting would rank nearly with pig-sticking at the top of the poll. The man on the expensive horse, if he is a proud man, may get an amount of pleasure; and the rider of genius, if he is not a proud man, may get the same satisfaction out of a cheap mount. The genius will always contrive to see the hounds, though I don't believe any amount of dexterity can keep him in the first flight if his horse isn't the right stamp. Now, in my case, I am unfortunately proud and impecunious. I can't afford the horses and I don't like being behind. Hunting stays on a border line the whole time, so that I ask myself, when balancing the minimum budget (which would get one a rod in a salmon river) against the pleasures obtained, whether it is worth while.

If it is true that the corner stones of sport are skill and personal danger, then I don't think that the *field* is enjoying the highest of the arts. For the huntsman it is probably the greatest thing in the world. His skill is of the highest, his responsibility heavy, and the danger not inconsiderable. But for the simple follower, who does not exercise the art of hunting hounds, I don't think there is much skill involved. Merely to ride a horse over English hunting fences, provided he is a good horse, does not need genius. Nor, if he is a good horse, is the danger apparent.

In my case, as a less than average horseman on a cheap mount in a difficult country, the issues become obscured. To begin with, there is the question of emulation: the bugbear of all sports. I am by nature inclined to emulate the jealous ranks of the first flight, however much I may try not to. In the first place, I doubt whether Silver ever could stay there, even if I were Geoffrey Brooke: in the second place, if I were that gentleman and could challenge the position, the danger would be immoderate. We should have to make up our mind to finish every hunt with an exhausted crumpler, and that quite early in the day.

Silver cost seventy pounds four years ago, and hunting the Duke's country on him is a specialised thing. If you are well placed to begin with, you have got to make up your mind whether you want to live with the first flight for ten minutes, or whether you want to see the end of the hunt somehow. You have got to firmly swallow your pride and fit in with the main body. So this has cancelled the possibility of excelling. What other joys remain? Well, the skill of mere riding is not excessive, as I said before, and the main body sees little of the huntsman's skill, so there is only the pleasure of danger left. Now danger, to be pleasant, demands reward. If a dangerous series of leaps is going to keep me in the first flight, they will be worth while. But when I have to take my risks merely to keep with the main body, then the expenses of hunting, even at a minimum, begin to merit consideration.

I no longer get much pleasure out of wearing a top hat, or fancying my position in the top drawer: so this form of excellence has gone also. One might ask what remains.

I don't know: but something does remain and keeps one hunting. The relationship with one's horse is pleasant: and jumping has a residuum of skill and beauty all its own, or one wouldn't skylark unobserved on the way home: and danger is a tonic, even unrewarded. I have always said that

the best way of curing depressions over love affairs, finan-
cial matters, or ill-health, is to give oneself a good fright.

In this week's *Field* there are two interesting articles: one
golden piece of reflection by Major Carlos Clarke, and one
effusion by a person whose name I don't care to remember. Clarke writes about the horrible person who,
when asked if he had a good hunt, says: 'Yes, I was fifth all
the way.' But the other article was the one that made me
think. The writer refers to a 'notorious funker' and proceeds to tell a story about his humiliation. It is a cruel
story. It made me wonder what 'funking' was. Take four
extremes: (1) The imaginative man on the cheap horse, (2)
the unimaginative man on the cheap horse, (3) the imaginative man on the £500 hunter, (4) the unimaginative
man on the £500 hunter.

No. 1 is in danger and knows it: is he a funker if he sees
little of the first flight? No. 2 is in danger and does not
know it: will he acquire merit by breaking his neck, and,
however brave, will he even by *able* to get into the front,
considering his horse? No. 3 has got the ace of trumps in
his hand (the £500 horse) and, however timorous, he must
realise it. So he is not doing anything particularly magnificent if he goes well. No. 4 can produce no excuse for not
being at the head of the hunt. Now, which of these men is
going to be blamed for what? Take the argument a step
further. Cut out the horses altogether, or give them all the
best. What is 'funking' anyway? Presumably the 'funker'
is behaving as God made him behave. His imagination is
what he was born with. Why should he be despised?
Perhaps a single jump is a steeplechase to his dilating eye.
No. 4, with the brains of a tipsy wood-louse, may see no
terror in a double oxer wired both sides; the funker may
see death in a ditch. It is the thing seen that counts.

The meet was at Sirewick. There were two separate
hunts; and here is another funny thing about hunting with
the Duke's. Suppose there are from 150 to 200 people out,

and suppose we are drawing Howling Wood. We are
stretched out in a line half a mile long, in a ride. The fox
goes away at the top end. How is the back end of the line to
arrive in the first flight? In the two hunts I had a taste of
both extremes. Hunt number one found me at the tail of
the start, and I rode a line of gates, on a slow horse, to
Deerhands. I think I had two leaps. As a matter of fact, I
committed an error of judgment, because there was one
stiff place which I might have gone over (nobody else
noticed it, or thought it worth while), and this might have
brought me up a bit. However, I couldn't have done
much. Hunt number two found me angry at having got to
Deerhands after a couple of friends who don't go very
well; but it also found me reasonably placed. Two fences,
finding my own leaps, put me up in spite of Sparks'
slowness, and I got into the field which saw the fox jink,
well placed. The leading bitch was then less than a yard
behind him. He got away in a hedge, however, and we
kept it up, with one check, for some time. It was fun. I
can't remember much about the geography (the only way
to know a country properly is to live, drive and shoot in it,
and the Friday country varies between eight and fifteen
miles from home) but there are little bits about the thing
itself. The funny thing about the fox was that it looked like
a hare. I have often mistaken hares for foxes, but never vice
versa. I suppose this must be because I have been shooting
them lately, and got accustomed to hares more than foxes.
Anyway, it was interesting. Then there was Purcell taking
a toss in wire (alongside a fellow who was doing the same)
at a fence that I was just over. There were several purlers,
including the Master. He remarked that his horse had
kicked him in the two hardest places, his head and his tail.
There was one of the whips, who didn't notice me near,
saying crossly to his horse at a ditch: 'Very well, then, fall
into it!' A human touch, intimate, and rare in one's
relations with a whip. There was Sparks' habit of taking a
mighty bound and arriving on all four feet, so that I had to

land far back in the saddle with the reins running through
my fingers. I suppose we must have had between a dozen
and twenty fences. There was a sad glimpse of three couple
of hounds chasing a rabbit. On second thoughts, I didn't
think it was sad. I was mainly surprised, partly amused,
and faintly annoyed. There was Luke Fieldfare coming up
from behind me at a check and saying that Sparks leapt
well; which gave pleasure because actually he didn't, and
some of it had been to my own credit. There was almost a
friendly attitude from other followers of the Duke's,
growing to know me in three years. And now it is sore to
sit down.

24. xi. xxxiv.

Hunting is good for human nature. Humanitarians in-
form me that the enjoyment of slaughter coarsens the soul.
They are not hunting humanitarians, and don't know that
at least half the people out avert their minds from the
kill—have been hunting an abstract fox. Nor am I convinced that the spectacle of natural slaughter does coarsen
the soul. It certainly makes life less highfaluting and more
real. But leave this aside and consider the advantages.

One animal has a most unpleasant time in his animal
way. Some thirty hounds have a glorious time, some two
hundred horses enjoy themselves, and two hundred human beings improve perceptibly. Take the aspects in
which they improve: they exercise the mental faculties of
wisdom and courage, and their bodies gather health. Anything that can make the upper classes take risks, however
minor, sharpen their wits, by matching their pre-vision
against the cunning of a fox, and improve their physical
health, by exerting themselves all day out of doors, is a
good thing. Besides this, two million people are kept in
direct and indirect annual employment; a breed of twenty
thousand hounds is maintained in the beauty of life, for
they would otherwise perish, being useless as pets; and the

whole thing is almost the only concern into which the capitalist puts his money (some £8,000 a year for each decent hunt) that is never run for profit. Even the entertainment given by a theatre manager is a capitalist (profit-giving) concern, but the two million grooms and saddlers yield no increment to their employers.

If my humanitarian (one once threw a book at me: and what is more, she hit me on the end of the nose) can be induced to admit any of these points, the next question raised is always as follows: 'Granted that hunting is a good thing, why not hunt a drag, as some people do, thus sparing the fox?' Well, you lose one of the corner stones: skill. I understand that there is no skill in handling hounds to a drag. But what to the mere follower is much more important, you lose reality. You are beginning to play at let's pretend, like contract bridge for love, and, still more unfortunate, you are losing the element which I may call 'human.' When you hunt with a drag you are sure of a run, and can only exercise the skill of riding in it. But when you hunt the fox, you are not sure of a run. You may have a blank day, are up against a large number of uncertainties, and you *achieve* something, if things go well, which is not achieved with aniseed. It is the perennial difference between the partridge and the clay pigeon.

At last we come to the fox himself. Two ridiculous things are commonly said about him. The colonel with a high blood-pressure says: 'The little beggar enjoys being hunted.' The spinster in Bognor Regis replies: 'Imagine yourself being pursued across the Russian Steppes by a pack of howling wolves.' The truth, as usual, lies between the extremes. It is useless to anthropomorphise the fox, comparing his emotions to the highly specialised ideative and imaginative reactions of the higher human centres. The degrees of terror are obviously different, in the fox's case instinctive, in the man's much more conscious and complex. The spinster is right, but only in a small way. So, curiously, is the colonel right—in a way as small. I

never believed this till I talked to Major Van der Byl of
Wappenham. He told me a story something like this: 'A
woman wrote to me asking how I should like to be the
quarry. I replied that I had been, in the Boer War, and that
though the sensation was highly unpleasant I would not
have missed it for the world.' Now the major is the kind of
man who advocates flogging for cruelty to animals (on the
old bogus story about the garotters) and this makes me see
red: he is also himself firmly opposed to the belief that the
fox enjoys being hunted at all. But the curious result of his
story has been to convert me, if only a very little, towards
the belief that the fox does get a tiny edge of satisfaction.
For I can absolutely see that it must have been worth while
being chased by Boers—if one got away. The fox, in fact,
is exercising skill just like the huntsman; and I do not
believe it is possible to be skilful without some kind of
satisfaction. The fox is afraid to his ancestral bones, in his
animal way; but somewhere there is a tiny flame of working skill, which, if he survives, must warm his panting
heart a little. And, according to Van der Byl, six times out
of seven he does escape.

25. xi. xxxiv.

There is one more excuse for hunting (though I should
do it, excusably or not) and that is that the fox has got to be
kept down somehow, for the good of the farmer. Now
there are three ways of keeping him down, besides hunting. You can trap, poison, or shoot. I have shot a fox
myself, in an unhunted country. I was coming stealthily
round the corner of a wood in the evening, hoping to get a
shot at a rabbit sprinting back to cover from far out in the
field. There was a hedge on my left, with a gate in it, which
I looked over. There, loping down the far side of the
hedge, was a fox who positively glowed in the twilight.
He was a big fellow, beautiful and catching at the heart
with excitement. I stood in a haze of indecision, but the

man who was with me whispered 'Shoot.' This was a shooting country. I waited till he was point-blank, less than twenty yards, and shot him from in front. He turned a somersault, and got up with a broken leg. He went off sideways, keeping about the same distance and still making for the wood. My elder said: 'It is all right. He will fall in a second.' He was going quite slow. I said: 'Shoot him with your air-gun.' It was a B.S.A. I heard the pellet thump him on the head with a heavy noise. The fox shook his head. But now he must have been at 25 yards and I was desperate. I gave him the other barrel, and he turned over two or three times. Then he got up and faded into the wood. We ran at once, and found blood, and the place where he had gone in. But it was thick wood, and though we searched for an hour we never found that living fox. He was doomed to die of gangrene, for a fox is one of the few animals of this type which do not lick their wounds.

Now all this happened long ago, it must be ten years, and I was led astray, and perhaps I may be forgiven. But the point of the story is that it is not particularly merciful to shoot foxes with shot-guns. And it is always dangerous to shoot in England with rifles, besides being increasingly difficult to hit a moving mark.

I can fairly say that if I was a fox, who enjoyed under hunting the sporting chance of escape (80 per cent. as defined by Van de Byl), I should prefer to be hunted; rather than to be left to rot with gangrene, or to gnaw my paw off in a steel trap, or to fear all food in case it should contain that fatal dusting of strychnine which would kill me in a writhing agony, curling my backbone till my mask touched my brush. If it comes to that, I should always prefer to die fighting (the hounds kill a fox in a second) and shall make a point of trying to knock down my gaolers, when they come to hang me for poisoning my future wife.

26. xi. xxxiv.

One tufted picked, and one down but irretrievable.

I keep making up my mind not to shoot at these creatures, but when they fly the temptation is great. A tufted duck seems so much more difficult to kill than a mallard: he has more vitality. You disable him, and he comes down with a splash, only to recover in a few seconds and begin swimming. You can follow him for hours in the punt, giving him broadside after broadside, but he dives and vanishes and reappears. He is as human as a penguin, too, which makes it worse. I don't feel that a mallard has much expression in his face, but a tufted has. I disabled and finally got up to a tufted last year; after a barrel in the air and two on the water had rendered him incapable of motion, and the look of pitiful terror in his lovely orange eye made me feel sick of myself, as if I were separate and recognised a leper. Besides, they bleed. Their soft tuxedo wells with bright red blood, as if you had butchered a child in evening dress: but a child, a pathetic soft thing with a plump breast. There is expression in its wild, agonised, pleading eye, and the business becomes revolting. I suppose I shall have to proscribe tufted in future. Does God, I wonder, suddenly decide that he can't go on giving diphtheria to children: Jefferies liked shooting, because it made him feel like God.

28. xi. xxxiv.

I couldn't get away till after one o'clock, and then never found the hounds. They were having a screaming day, in three hunting countries, from Ladcote to Tenmere and back to Park and Sisters Singleton and then to Thorns. They knocked off at about 1.30 with hounds scattered all over the country, all the second horses lost, and only half a dozen with them. One of the Locks girls had fallen and lost her glasses—amusing to see her groping for them, like a

flamingo fishing—and Luke Fieldfare sprained his ankle,
falling on tarmac. My miserable party of latecomers kept
gathering stragglers, like a snowball, with wild conflicting
reports and lonely figures silhouetted on misty skylines.
Not much fun for us.

They must have hunted over the site of the only
measurable battle that has been fought in the Shire.
Cymbeline fought it at Thorns. The Romans beat him,
and he retreated across the eel-full river. They buried the
common soldiers indiscriminately; but there are a couple
of tumuli on the river bank, perhaps the graves of chiefs.
They stick up, green bubbles of grass. Antiquarians of the
nineteenth and eighteenth centuries have poked about
amongst them. Hedgers have ruminated on them with
inquiring eyes. The old bones lie there, reddish with the
dye of the soil, among rusty scraps of weapons, and to-day
the bright hoofs battered above them: to-day the iron
flashed, the red coats glowed in the grey Shire afternoon,
over the brittle, porous, rosy bones.

30. xi. xxxiv.

And here was a miserable day, if ever there was. I upset
myself scrambling to work, and start the car, and collect
boots, and dress in time. Then I ate two biscuits in the car,
and felt sick, just as I used to do in the nursery over the
excitement and bother of travelling by train. The mist was
cold, disheartening. You could just see one field. It was
not a day to make you go; and I stood about, lonely,
waiting for the horse, whilst the county talked to itself
across me.

We drew a covert beyond Badgers Cross-roads, whose
name I temporarily forget and don't care to know anyway.
We found. I was in my usual place at the tail, almost with
the second horseman, when he went off. So the next
desultory half-hour was a question of chasing the man in

front. We never saw the hounds for five minutes at a stretch, dodged under railway lines, stopped by brooks, baulked by females, no incentive to choose my own places: and didn't. I lack the guts to go at a bad bit unless I know it will put me with hounds. To do it merely because it and a couple more like it *may* put me *near* them, is too much.

Then things began to improve. The foul old hireling, Sparks, progresses at a rate of about four knots, and everybody passes us in the enclosures, but usually we can pick up again on the jumps. He was jumping heavily but safely and I began to warm up. The hunt overran itself, turned right-about, and there I was with nobody in front of me but Bishop. This looked better. We thumped and blundered over a couple more fences, now jumping in our own places. Sparks takes the easiest way, climbing where possible in preference to jumping, and jumping, when he must, from a slow trot or stand. Then we dropped our quarters in a far-side ditch, and scrambled out whilst the lady behind us said: 'Oh!' The two next fences were peculiarly slovenly. Then there was a wide enclosure in which the four knots dropped to two, although I nearly kicked his belly out. Then there was a check. We were walking up the side of a seed field when the horse went hopping lame. Standing, he would not put his near fore to the ground.

I asked my neighbour whether I ought to take him home. She said yes. I asked a farmer. He said yes. Then he blundered worse than ever, and everybody said yes, all round.

I took him home. By the time we had gone two miles he was perfectly sound, and we came into the stables like a bell.

I had left them at Deerhands.

So to-day is: cold fog and sickness; cold feet; fences that were plainly visible, but not the wire in them; vacuity when things were beginning to go right; senseless return, brooding, bad.

A woman recognised Sparks. She said: 'Of course he is very old now, and in poor condition, but when we had him as a young horse he was a magnificent one. Yes, I know he is slow, but he used to be able to jump a house.'

On the way home I misquoted: 'Ready to be anything, in the ecstasy of being over, and as satisfied with six feet as the *moles* of Adrianus.'

8. xii. xxxiv.

Some time since the last entry and before to-day, I shot my first Shire teal. He was suddenly (though as a matter of fact it was a she) out of the octagon reeds and ten feet in the air. I believe I am right in supposing that a congeries of teal is called a 'spring.' It is an appropriate name. She may have had a mate. There seemed to be several things going on in the air at the same time, but there was no time to do anything except shoot her. I did not realise that she was a teal until I picked her out, after fetching the punt, and then I took one of her green-fringed feathers; which are metallic in *texture* as well as colour, like an exotic beetle.

A lovely day. It was a Park meet, and the morning was spent in a barrage of boys. We chopped our fox by surrounding him. Not much fun. It was from Painesborough Wood that the day improved. My sinus is hurting me too much for a connected account, though in this case I should have been able to give it. The day boiled down to two foxes. The first was found in the Foxley vicinity, with myself well placed. I went with the master and one other on the proper line, whilst the main body skirted. We soon found ourselves in an enclosure that could only be escaped in one direction, and this put us on the periphery of a circle with the main body at the centre and the fox half-way along the radius. So we had a cracking hunt back to Painesborough, with the fox dead beat just in front of us. It was Silver's first day. He had tried to buck me off at the

meet and was now leaping like an angel. He never touched
a twig, never had a lead, and never thought twice about it.

In Painesborough Wood we changed on to a fresh fox,
again magnificently placed, and went away for Mytton
Wood. My dud spot happened here, for I guessed the
Sisters Singleton side and went off alone on my own line to
the right. There was a covert between me and the rest of
the field, so that it took me five minutes to realise that
hounds had gone slap away on the other side. Then I set
out on a stern chase, with nothing visible in front. It meant
jumping gates and in and out of roads, but I was excited
and the old horse was going to go. I was within a field of
the half-dozen left with the hounds when we came to the
Southam brook, feeling delighted. The brook was wired
on the far side, the very one that I caught my trout in at the
beginning of the season. I tried leading the horse across a
thick plank, but he sensibly refused. Then I tried farther
up, and found two stragglers, stopped by the brook. But
at this place there were ten yards unwired. One of them
was in, and just climbing out on the far side. The other
said: 'Don't jump. You won't get across. Only three
people have tried it, and they all went in. The master was
one. The horses think they can walk across and don't leap
properly.' I said, knowing Silver's feelings about water,
'Mine won't think that, anyway.' I took a run of fifty yards
and got him into a full gallop. The late rain had filled the
brook to the brim. He spotted it ten yards away, stuck in
his toes, slithered seven yards, said in an audible voice:
'God, I can't stop!' and leaped into the air. It was interesting to see him disappear underneath me, with only his
head sticking out; and the water was warm. I scrambled
out on the far side and tried to pull him after me. But he
was stuck and pulled, too. My feet kept shooting from
under me, so that I sat down with a bump, like a clown in a
circus. The fellow on the other side tried not to smile.
Silver stayed in for half an hour, and cost me nine shillings
in tips, and went home lame, and I smashed the patent bit,

and wrecked my top hat, and missed the last part to Mytton. But it was a grand day.

I never went properly into a brook before, partly because it is impossible to get Silver to go at one if he had seen that particular bit, and it is a sensation which I can recommend. To begin with, it is easy falling. You don't have to turn head over heels and perhaps get a rap on the head, nor do you get that split second's inverted view of a belly, muddled up with some hoofs, nor do you wonder absent-mindedly whether your ribs will crackle. In fact, the horse does all the falling himself. He sinks into his cloud of spray with a surprised expression. All you have to do is to go down with your ship.

9. xii. xxxiv.

Silver is a dear old boy, and we get along pretty well together. A year on him when I first bought him in the Scurry country, and three seasons since that here; we have rubbed off corners mutually. He causes me some embarrassment by forging in public, by tumbling over molehills, and by refusing water always and fences if not feeling fit. Originally I used to think that my bad riding was responsible for these weaknesses; but now I doubt it. I used to flog him at the brooks until I was sick, but I never got him over anything beyond a certain size: not after the first time when it was possible to take him by surprise. I used to get a certain number of falls through insisting. There was a day two seasons ago, for instance, when he was feeling under the weather. I insisted on some timber with a slippery take-off and a boggy bit on the landing side. I saw the bad landing, and put on steam to make him clear it, and he couldn't afford the speed as well as the rise, and we hit the top rail. I had two falls that day, high, wide and handsome, and brought him home lame. Now I don't trouble. If he feels well we go fair. If he feels ill we have to go twice at a fence, the first a prospecting tour, and we give up at the mere sight of water. It is an ignoble but a pleasant life.

10. xii. xxxiv.

This new, and I am sure very unsporting, acquiescence in Silver's judgment has few ill consequences. We see about as much of a hunt as we ever did, and never seem to fall down. A fall, says Surtees somewhere, is a hawful thing.

11. xii. xxxiv.

Among the happiest hours of this happy winter have been the long teas at Tom Bourne's, when he insists that I come in after shooting. It is fine to sit down tired, in muddy gaiters by a hospitable fire, and to spread the butter thick, whilst Tom talks about the parish news. The great thing about country news is that it is timeless. The fact that Annie Madders has had a baby four months after matrimony (but Mrs. Primrose is sure that it was a seven months child: which seems an extenuating circumstance) merges into the behaviour of the German gentleman who lived by the ridings till 1917, and was believed to be a spy. This in turn leads to a cruel trick practised by the second marquis in 1750.

The countryside itself changes. Such and such a nobleman planted that grove of trees over there, in order to save himself the ignoble spectacle of such and such a farm. The grassy footpath over there was a main avenue once. The barn over by so-and-so's was part of a monastery, and you can see the gothic window in the east wall, filled in with wattle and daub, and it has a secret passage. Mr. Reynolds has had a new fireplace put in at the Queen's Arms.

News of the past is as gentle as news of the present. It is also as rare. I am grateful to the ghost of the suicide who was staked down at the crossroads by Oxen's Halt, just as I am grateful to Rut's greyhounds for eating Mrs. Warm's cat. Nothing changes very much, and when it does we consider it deeply. The institution has cut down one of its famous beech trees to build a pavilion. 'Anybody,' says Tom, 'can build a pavilion, but you can't build a beech.'

12. xii. xxxiv.

Another of the higher country pleasures is associated with the shooting dog. The two best local dogs are Luke Fieldfare's Timmy, a golden cocker, and Fred Aytoun's Belle (or Mother) a black labrador. Belle is ten years old, steady and nearly blind: Timmy is in his first season, constantly being smacked. Both are far more intelligent than a Christian, or at least than a clergyman. Sometimes, in a crisis, they are put on the same runner in a hedge: and then you can see Timmy working by inspiration, Belle by system. Timmy's small golden stump is wriggling with excitement, while Belle's blind old nose fades quietly up and down the ditch. When he finds the bird he takes it with a little pounce: when she gets the certain smell there is no acceleration. She walks on to it without a tremor, picks it like a gentle nursemaid, and delivers it to hand before you know it has been found.

13. xii. xxxiv.

An argument started in the Queen's Arms at Warden, about safe bets. One farmer said that a sure way of making money was by betting somebody that he couldn't eat a pigeon a day for a month. There is no catch in this. Apparently the bird simply becomes nauseating. This was capped by three other gastronomic curiosities: that nobody can eat a pound of cheese, neat, in a minute, nor drink a pint of beer and eat an arrowroot biscuit in the

same time, nor drink a pint of beer every hour throughout the day.

The best bet known to me is connected with a sporting gun. Make a man look down the barrel from the breech end, and bet him four to one that he can't judge the length of the recessed chamber for the cartridges. He usually concludes that it can't be shorter than the cartridges, or they wouldn't go in; can't be the same length, or you wouldn't be offering four to one; and therefore must be a little longer. He takes out one of his own cartridges, measures it, adds a few sixteenths according to his fancy, and puts down his money. As a matter of fact there is no recessed chamber. The barrel is of the same calibre all the way to the choke, and the apparent cartridge-cylinder is an optical delusion connected with what I suppose is a powder ring. The best of the bet comes when you leave him to pry for the non-existent ridge, first with his finger and then with a pencil.

26. xii. xxxiv.

An obvious fact, which is not generally realised, is that a forging horse does not strike the heel of his forehoof with the toe of his hind. He strikes toe to toe.

27. xii. xxxiv.

The sun rises at 8.7. The winter has drawn in. Jimmy shot one tufted drake. We had five rabbits over the week-end, afternoons.

Jimmy was in the band of the Scots Guards most of his life, so we have developed a means of communication by bugle calls for joint marauding expeditions. With him on one side of the lake and myself on the other, it is useful to whistle

when I want him to move on, or

when I want him to go quicker.

If it is no good waiting any longer, we blow

followed by

By using these calls (Charge, Trot, Cease Fire, and
Close) one can meet almost any shooting emergency in
which the other gun is invisible. Halt, Gallop, Retire and
Walk are also useful.

28. xii. xxxiv.

Two seasons ago I put up at a farmhouse in order to get
my Christmas hunting. The farmer celebrated my arrival
by slaughtering a pig, and for the rest of my stay I was
regaled with pork sausages, pork chops, pork kidneys,
and pork. This would have been fine, except that pork and
arsenic are synonymous for me. But the interesting thing
was the baths.

The sanitation in this farm was very properly outdoor
(good for the health and philosophy) and there was no
bathroom. It was a wettish season and after hunting I

wanted to bathe. Remembering a bath in Surtees, I reverted to my ancestors with pleased anticipation. On hunting days the lady of the house was instructed to light a fire in the bedroom, put a hip bath in front of it, and surround the whole with a barricade of towel horses.

They were the best baths of my life; and bathing, along with the lighting of fires, is among the highest arts. It was to no tyro in the mysteries of ablution that this ancestral experience appealed.

In order to enjoy a real hip bath, the fire and the towel horses to trap its heat are essential. The bather then lies upon his back in four inches of water, with the bath fitting him from the nape of the neck to the curve of the posterior, and puts his feet upon the mantelpiece. A sponge, constantly replenished with hot water, is placed upon the abdomen, and the twinkling flames are watched between the legs. Since the air of the room is as warm as the water, exposure to it is unnoticeable. The firelight promotes meditation: there are hot cans by the tubside to stimulate the water at intervals: the winter night ('Good-night,' you said to the last person hacking home) is cold outside: and when the time comes for dressing, the English coal dries your saffron body automatically, steaming from the pink knuckles of your knees.

29. xii. xxxiv.

Ten days in bed with a sinus, Christmas at home, and now Silver is fresh as a lark. To-day was a baffled series of circles round Deerlands: scent obviously quite fair in covert, but apparently miserable outside. His lordship was hunting hounds. Tom Close said to me: 'A good huntsman ought to be in a literal sense a master of hounds, a hound-master. He ought to be the "head hound," more or less. The pack must look to him for control and drive, imposed by his personality. His discipline and leadership must be towards the hounds what the leadership of the kind of person who is called "a leader of men" is towards the men he leads. That is why Bishop is a good huntsman. An amateur huntsman is often easy-going, and the hounds are slack with him, just as little boys in a prep. school would be with a characterless master. Of course, the dogs may be more difficult to lead than the bitches, but when a "head hound" has them two days a week he makes them go. In packs where they get a "slack" day with an amateur once a week, they can't be pulled together properly on the other day.'

This was interesting and obviously true, except that I should personally (from the prep. school analogy) call it more a matter of personality or character than of discipline. The ideal huntsman is not necessarily 'unkind' or 'severe.' The essential is personality.

It was the kind of day that kept beginning and never went on. There were very few out. I only saw two falls: one of the whips, and Mrs. Borzoi. Although it was a dud day, I enjoyed it much. It was a surprise to find that ten days in bed didn't make one cut a voluntary. Silver went magnificently (in a double bridle, as an experiment), never looked twice at anything, and kept me well up in the little bursts. Finally, the whole field got left in Deerlands, whilst the master went on alone in a silent private run to the Forest.

The ground is very deep just now, and the rides unpleasant.

Silver took one stile quite beautifully, lifting his quarters over it with a foot to spare.

Hacked home with Mrs. Gore. She is a very nice person. Although I suppose she is technically one of the grand old ladies of the Duke's, you keep catching quite a perfect little girl peeping sideways out of her eyes.

Mrs. Gore said to me: 'There is a saying about the Duke's that three seasons in its first flight are enough to break anybody's nerve.' I find this difficult to sort out.

Either one is in the first flight because one can afford the type of horse and is a reasonable horseman (in which case why should one be frightened?) or else one is a bold man but not on a good horse: in which case why aim at the first flight, if risky? I suppose the soldiery from Bredon must vie with one another considerably, and make it impossible not to take a place, whatever the mount; and hence the adage. In any case, I never see the first flight, so needn't bother my head about this.

30. xii. xxxiv.

I look forward to old age, and the opportunity of laying down the law without contradiction. One of the better openings for this kind of declamation will be the comparative merits of hunts. It would be amusing to take a circular tour, like Mr. Sponge, and write a book about it. I have hunted with five packs, but with only two sufficiently to be able to make comparisons. I looked up old hunting journals to-day, and compiled a statistic out of one of them. In this book I had hunted nine days with the Scurry, nineteen with the Duke's, and once with the Warden. The Scurry killed an average of one fox every day, and the average guess was twenty-seven fences a day. The Duke's killed a fox every other day, and my average of fences was only nine. I have omitted club-hunting.

I started counting fences, not strictly, but in vague lumps of half a dozen at checks, and so on, as a result of a bet with a groom in the East Sussex. The largest number I ever had was between sixty and seventy, unless I exaggerated in those days, and that was with the Scurry. With the Duke's I never had more than thirty. These statistics apply to one-horse days, in which I generally stopped before three o'clock. The Scurry day was on one horse, but I stayed out until they went home, and put the horse off his feed for a fortnight.

It seems, therefore, that if one is hunting to kill foxes or to jump fences, the Scurry is a better hunt than the Duke's. The snag comes in when you consider the run itself. The Scurry seems in retrospect to have been such a crowded country. You could never run straight for long, but were into the next place or a tarmac road or headed or circling before you knew where you were. Also I can't remember that the Scurry often ran at our pace. It is all very confused. In those days I was better mounted on the average, and I certainly went with little or no discrimination. I have a retrospective picture of myself careering along in the wake of the hounds, falling off like the White Knight at every refusal. I certainly rode the line, jumped a great deal and saw much more of hounds than I do now. All this was partly due to the country. It was closer fenced than the Duke's, so that you could get two or more of the Scurry enclosures into every one of our vast prairies; and so jumping was doubled. I must have seen the hounds more because they were slower, but also because the contours themselves were on a smaller scale and more up and down. Half the time with the Duke's you can only see the field you are actually in, with a whopping great fence at the end of it.

It is funny the way my local snobs sneer at the old Scurry. I shouldn't like to go back there (I should like to stay in the Duke's with a horse that cost £500), but I don't know that I didn't have a better time on Silver there than I do on Silver here. Certainly I can't remember queueing at gates and low places half so often as we do here. I suppose the fences were smaller on the average. But what's the use of big fences if you don't jump them? The Duke's has a regular queue-population.

I shouldn't like to go back, but it was a jolly country. You zigzagged about in it like a bluebottle in a jam-jar. I was amused by several days in the old book, and here is one of them, fairly typical:

'By train to Adamsbridge, and hacked over to Four Oaks. Mare: Freckles. A fierce frost overnight, and every-

thing white this morning. The sun got warm at 10.30 and
hounds moved off at the usual time, with the fields thaw-
ing. It developed into a bright morning with little wind
and bright sun. Cooler in the afternoon. We drew covert
after covert fruitlessly from Four Oaks and Ash Wood. It
was such a bright day that the disappointment was bear-
able, although we were drawing blank over beautiful lines
of country from the point of view of hunting. I think it was
about half-past two that we found a fox in Whitecastle
Wood. From then till hounds went home at five o'clock
we were hunting practically continuously, but in a scrappy
circular way, though the runs were over good country.
Between thirty and forty fences. The grey mare carried me
well. We went from Whitecastle Wood to Fusileers, and
lost: from Beachbarn to Eastersill, and killed: from Beachbarn to Whitecastle Wood, and gave up. Three falls. The
first time the mare slid at a bad take-off, into the ditch on
the nearside of a fence. The second time she refused at the
last moment, at a jump with a greasy downhill take-off:
she refused, but I consented like a shot rabbit. We reas-
sembled and took the jump afterwards. The third time she
pecked at a drop fence. I dived smartly over her head, fell
in front of her forelegs, and she jumped neatly over me (so
that for her it was a sort of in-and-out) although I was
holding the reins. I was cutting these voluntaries because
Freckles takes a lot of kicking along, and generally whilst I
was kicking she was jumping. There was a man out with a
wooden leg. He falls off in the most natural way at every
fence, and gets on again, sometimes with his leg on back to
front.'

The very first of January, 1935.

I got up before 7. There were no duck on the lake, and
the snipe was absent from the Camford water. Bourne's
rushy wild, by the cabbages, was blank. Jimmy and I went
up to Three Woods, and split to go singly round the sides,

meeting at the top. I saw a pheasant go in almost at once, and went to the place in which I thought it had settled, without any particular hopes. The wood is hopelessly thick. However, this or another pheasant got up at long range, and I just had time to change my finger to the choke barrel. She was a hen, and I turned her over beautifully into the thickest of the undergrowth. I spent an hour trying to find her, tracing lines from the first big puff of feathers, to a further couple in a kind of thorny inferno, but in vain. At 10 we came away after I had lost my temper. At 10.5 we met a hare in a hedge and were both too surprised to fire. At 10.7 Jimmy shot a rabbit; and I missed, in a brambly ditch, what might have been a rabbit or might have been the hare. It is not even certain that I missed it. Everything was too dark, impenetrable and hellish to be properly sure. Anyway, I gave it up. At 10.30 we were driving back when we spotted a cock pheasant scooting across the road into my land. We stopped the car and surrounded him. However, he saw us both and got up almost out of range. I gave him both barrels hysterically, and he seemed to throw his head up a little for the first. He came down in the next spinney, beyond the Camford water. I ran to circumvent him, stalked the spinney inch by inch, spotted him crouching under a root as cunning as a tom cat. The usual internal struggle, then I retreated half a dozen paces and gave him the cylinder barrel sitting. He jumped a few inches and lay still, bleeding from the beak, a beautiful bundle of mahogany, an old spurred cock. I went back to Jimmy and lied that he was a broken-legged bird that I had to finish off as a runner.

After breakfast I went back to borrow Bourne's Pip to search for the first bird. Scent was hopeless. Pip got into something, and lost herself. This wood is a genuine *selva oscura*. One scratches oneself all over, staggers, almost cries, tussles like Laocoon. At last I found the dog and started back in a Livingstone-Stanley detour to a place where I *thought* I had seen a hen come in. On the way, with

boughs between my legs and brambles round my neck, I
thought I saw a woodcock, but had no chance to fire. It
was a brownish silent blur that banked. It may have been
an owl. Pip worked beautifully. In the very patch where I
had expected the pheasant, there she was. But I was far off.
She got up very quietly and there was a tree between us. I
changed to the choke, thought she was out of range,
waited for the tree, and turned her over. Both this shot and
the first gave me a shock, but I dare say that a closely-
packed wood of trees makes distances seem larger. In this
case also Pip failed to find; but luckily I walked into her
stone dead, a dark-coloured bird.

I am invited to Milton on Saturday.

2. i. xxxv.

Silver had a saddle sore, healed, from May's side saddle,
and a dead ringworm. I had lent him whilst I was ill. He
looked poor, seemed apathetic at the meet, did not even
break into a canter when we first got on to grass. The first
fence disposed of the first whip, who took a long time
catching his horse. He took it at some rails. I took it at the
hedge, and seemed to make Silver grunt a little, landing
with my weight too far back on his loins. The second fence
was a biggish drop with water on the far side. He refused. I
stayed ten minutes beating him, but not through rage:
with judgment. I tried everything—walk, trot, canter,
even stand. He merely stood up on end, flatly refusing
even to face it. Hounds came back in a circle. I gave in and
joined up. The third fence was a perfectly fair unditched
hedge. He refused again. We stayed twenty minutes, trying everything with the utmost patience. Then I gave in. I
told the groom that the horse was not fit. The groom was
furious. I was furious. Silver packed up. I went home and
apologised to the groom's wife.

There was one good fall. A fellow in scarlet, with no
horse visible, propped up on two knees and a shoulder just

behind me, at some fence which I seem to have taken without mentioning it above. He kind of lifted himself with his shoulder and then collapsed on it again. I hurried off, to evade the inquest and catching the horse, thinking he had broken his collar bone. Met him later being led back: face all bloody, back muscles torn, concussed.

But rage and despair were the keynote. I turned home at 12.30.

4. i. xxxv.

Queer day, officially piloting May on her first hunt for eight years. She had a very slow horse, which jumped well. We managed to show her a good deal of the run, and to bring her up to hounds for the last bit, in a wide semicircle from Weston to Sherborne Park in the Warden country. There was one good line of about half a dozen fences, but the rest rear guard and desultory. The good line was what brought us up. By two o'clock May was purple in the face. She packed up whilst hounds were running, and I stopped, too, not to discourage her on this important date in her life story. I enjoyed it, on the whole: especially as there was some talk of Luke Fieldfare piloting her, and he vanished throughout the Weston-Sherborne point, through taking a wrong turning. Did he fall or was he pushed?

Silver went better, but nothing like the performance of the earlier hunts, when he was fresh from good summer grass (particularly good and not-mere-fat-producing this summer) and the going was less deep. He was sliding at his fences and just tripping over them. However, only one refusal. Over timber he lifted himself like a snipe. Some of this may have been due to the leather jockey's switch which I carried instead of a crop: not a bad scheme. Good enough.

5. i. xxxv.

It was the Milton Saturday, with twelve guns, the last pheasant day of the season. We had something over a hundred birds between us. Two-thirds of the guns were lame and the rest asthmatic, but it was a revelation to see them shoot. All the birds collected in their last corners, and then began getting up like a feu de joie. I don't know whether it was having been ill, or a desire to excel and consequent poking, or sheer incompetence; but I only got four birds all day, and this made me miserable. The birds were surprisingly silent, coming from distances, and they curled over beautifully, head under, body over, tail round, as the other guns shot them. I remember one bird, hard hit, wriggling in the air above me in the effort to go on, like a chinese dragon. The grey long-tailed flakes floated out of the high woods, to be curled up in delayed puffs before you heard the bang.

I don't know what I was doing wrong. I was probably poking and pulling to the right, and the birds directly over me seemed to be a bother. It was a humiliation; but as I always do it at a big shoot I had better get accustomed to the feeling. I don't get enough shots at pheasants.

I think it is Richard Jefferies who has an interesting theory about the high bird vertically over you. He says that the human eye can bisect a horizontal line easily, but not a vertical one. Try bisecting the corner-of-a-room wall by eye, and then bisect the floor line for comparison.

I tried to console myself by reflecting that at Milton lived an uncle of Catherine Parr, Henry's sixth and surviving wife: he was made Lord Parr of Milton. And here also, I reflected, were several virgates which belonged to that Judith, niece of the Conqueror, who betrayed the son of Old Siward. Two black hearts, but I think mine was the blacker, went out to each other across the centuries.

Milton is one of the great houses that preserves. There seem to be no points of comparison between this great kind of shooting and my own, but it is lovely to have a little of it now and then. It is lovely, for one thing, to see a troop of keepers again: their weathered hands and faces, their tough boots, their rainproof clothes, their sure movements. Keepers seem to look after their masters like nurses. It always amuses me to see a man carrying a gun or some cartridges for another grown man who is going to use them. Then there is the luxury of a shooting luncheon, with an appetite for the tasty food and the sloe gin, and a roaring fire in a barn or a parlour to eat it by, and jolly company, and out again to the suffocating excitement of the big drives, and the flakes floating over from far or leaping up from near, so quick, in the last minute, that you have to let birds go by.

6. i. xxxv.

The only way I could get in on Tom's shooting was this: We agreed that I should pay him a negligible sum of money in return for it, on condition that he joined any shooting party he cared to, and we divided the game. But what a circus to divide it. We split up the first day evenly (I think he did it to see how I behaved), and since then he has resolutely refused to touch a feather. The result is that the whole thing is run on a system of subterfuge. Tom sneaks off and dumps the bag in the back of my car when he thinks I'm not looking. I sneak out to 'fetch my pipe' after tea, and hide a fair half (or the particularly rare and beautiful pheasant) in a corner behind the separator. Tom comes out to see us off in the dark, and detects a certain complaisance in my demeanour, and smells out the pheasant like a working terrier. Just as I am letting in the clutch there is a series of loud and furious yells. The car accelerates with a riot of detonations; but Tom runs like a stag. The speedometer needle is rising fifteen. The pheasant lands in the seat beside me, with a satisfied thump.

7. i. xxxv.

Milton again, with the same guns nearly. A general, a colonel, and a captain, all excellent shots; another captain, and the host moderate; a youth, name unknown, and a one-legged gentleman called Weakly. Also 2 keepers carrying guns. This made 8 official shooters, plus 2 unofficially. We were doing a last general clean-up, and got 32 pheasants, 21 brace partridges, nine hares and a couple of rabbits. This makes a series as follows: Friday, 280 pheasants, no partridges; Saturday, 120 pheasants, 7 brace partridges; Monday, 32 pheasants, 21 brace partridges, 9 hares. To-day I killed 3 brace partridges, 3 hares. As usual I missed every pheasant of the four that came to me. I suppose I shall have to get psycho-analysed. Of the partridges I had one left and right, single birds, ten yards apart.

I enjoyed myself. It was an odd thing, but I suddenly found myself limping in sympathy with the rest.

Damn the pheasants.

Alas!

Just lack of experience of this grand kind of shooting, I suppose.

8. i. xxxv.

There is one way of affording to hunt and fly, and that is to do them. Something will turn up. It is the same with money. The way to earn it is to spend it in advance: then you have got to earn it or go bust.

12. 1. xxxv.

Waiting fruitlessly for duck on the octagon to-night, as I do often, without entering it in this journal, like a cat by an empty bowl of goldfish, I found that the moon was throwing my shadow on the blue snow. It moved beside me, the straight line of the gun barrel by my right foot, an iridescent deception of a line, a mirage that one looked at twice to be sure, a cold moonlight spectrum.

14. i. xxxv.

Martin came with Tom Bourne, Jimmy Warm and myself. We went up at 6.30 to the lakes for duck; to Three Woods at 10.30 for the wood; back again to walk the hedges with Pip at 2.30. Meals at home. We had 1 cock pheasant, 1 hen mallard, 2 woodcock, 1 hare, 2 rabbits. I was lucky and shot all but the pheasant and one of the rabbits. There are six woodcock in Three Woods, 2 snipe in the bog, 1 snipe at Camford Water. These must be seen to.

Totting up my records for this season, I find that we have killed 97 head of all sorts on my tiny rough shoot so far, of which I have killed 49. In shoots to which I have been invited, we have killed 363 head of game, of which I have killed 49.

I can't help feeling that to-day's bag has its own kind of fascination. No doubt I should have a tremendous shoot if I were a millionaire, and I dare say I should get bored with it. But here, where you have to rise with the sun, and walk all day, and earn what you kill, and be satisfied with little or nothing, it does become a kind of achievement to make one's own little gamut. We only killed seven things, but they included five separate species, and we saw six. Each shot was a separate affair, widely spaced from the last in point of time, and earned by the exercise of one's own legs. This *workmanlike* type of shooting trains one to a special kind of shot. One doesn't become a *great* shot, like the automatic butcher at the battle; in fact, one remains, in comparison with this type, a very poor shot indeed. But I think one keeps a kind of emotional advantage. It must become boring to be a great shot, who stands whilst the keepers deliver. For one thing, it must become easy. And when easy it ceases to be satisfactory, like all the other achievements.

15. i. xxxv.

Martin shot one pheasant and self one rabbit. There were eight pheasants roosting in one tree, but this is the time of year when the pheasant's novelty begins to lose its flush. It is the woodcock and the snipe that steal the lustre. I was far too pleased yesterday, after killing two 'cock, to be able to trust myself in writing about it. But the fact is that I am a good shot at 'cock, probably because as an emotional shooter it suits me to fire quickly, without giving law. I seem to kill them before they have begun to slip, as snipe and woodcock do.

They are both difficult birds to shoot and where I was brought up there used to be a rumour of a half-crown sweep on every 'cock. The lucky man received half-a-crown from each of the other guns. I tried to persuade them yesterday to give me some money; but they wouldn't.

16. i. xxv.

Self 4 rabbits, Bourne 6, 4 dug. Sis digs with what is called a 'navigator,' a narrow gouge-like spade that seems to cut more fiercely than its flat brother and is handy besides being almost unbreakable (by roots, etc.) for this type of work. The name must come from the same root as the word 'navvy.' The Navvies were the original work-men on the eighteenth-century Inland Navigation Canals, the greatest of poachers, and I suppose they dug with 'navigators.'

17. i. xxxv.

The record of this shooting season is an instructive one, which gives cause to think when one reads it over. However much I may have tried not to be a jealous shot, the fact remains that I record my own bags with greater interest than the total bags, and it has not made very interesting reading. In fact, shooting tends to be the most competitive of the sports, and for that reason I think the worst of them. I prefer not to suppress the excuses for missing and the long unjustified shots and the ducks that died slowly unretrieved, and counting my own heads. Not that these things are essential in shooting, only they are more difficult to evade than in the other sports. There is as much beauty in shooting as there is anything else, and the gamekeeper, or anybody who takes a gun round by himself, or an instinctively unselfish man, if there is such a thing, can enjoy it purely. Its beauties vary. You start on the bright stubbles of September (if you are not lucky enough for the grouse) with their little blue-and-white clouds and just a nip in the morning air. You may end in the snow, waiting for duck before dawn. It is probably the shooting man who takes most interest in the byways of nature: whether woodcock carry their young, or adders swallow them, whether flies settle directly on the ceiling, and all the rest of it. He should take an interest in the question of cruelty.

I talked to Major Van der Byl of Wappenham about this, and though I don't see eye to eye with him on some points, there is a tremendous amount in his line of thought. What I see in it, is the improvement of sport. He himself is by no means a pure sentimentalist or anti-sportsman. I have shot with him, he fishes, and he has hunted with some thirty packs of hounds. The advantage of obviating as much cruelty as possible in sports hinges on the question of art. If you make a point of killing your birds dead, you have got to make yourself a better shot, you have got to improve your art. Your objective, the clean kill, is going to be more difficult than the random wound, and if more difficult, therefore more satisfactory in achievement. Take, for instance, the question of the hunted fox. The wits of perhaps fifteen couple of hounds, three hunt servants, and a large number of horsemen are pitted against the wits of the animal. It is not so easy as it sounds, and the fundamental pleasure lies in conquering the difficulty by achieving a kill. Now Van der Byl says, and I think very justly, that the achievement is lowered by the holloa from outside. Not only is the fox pursued by this imposing train, but he is thwarted in his strategies by every chance bicyclist, motorist, or farm labourer that vocalises his passage and gives the game away. Disallow the holloa: leave the work to whose actually engaged upon it: if scent is poor and you can't kill, admit it: and fox-hunting becomes more difficult, more of an achievement, a more satisfying art. This is why the 'sporting chance' is not the nonsense of choleric Anglo-Indian colonels, but a practical philosophy.

Look at fishing. It seems at first an obscure and curious fact that the 'high hats' scorn the fisherman who kills trout on a worm. They are really saying, with profound subconscious reason, that the worm is too easy to give pleasure.

Then adopt the anti-cruelty line. It is astonishing how it justifiably raises the difficulty all round. Live-baiting is obviously very cruel: it is also easy. Abolish live-baiting and you will have your angler *spinning* for his pike. Instead of sitting with the vacuity of a float-fisher, he will be practising an art, working for his fish in a series of not unskilful casts.

Obviate the cruelty of the artificial stalk in the deer forest, in which after the difficulty of approach has been overcome by the ghillie the boring coup de grace is administered by a parasitic employer, and you may have some right to jump for joy at the gralloch.

Study, as they do, the humanity of killing a pig quickly,

and the art of pig-sticking rises.

The true sportsman is nearly always humane. He catches a tarpon (which is inedible) in Florida, and takes one scale from it and lets it go. This sort of thing provokes the amusement of the urban pleb, just like the old joke about the untouchables chasing the uneatables. But it is the apex of one kind of sport: an art pursued entirely for its own satisfaction.

One could produce quite a list of sporting practices which ought to be discouraged in the interest of sport. I should like to see the digging up of foxes that have got to ground abolished. There are three main reasons which are generally adduced in extenuation of this practice. First, the hounds may need blood. The answer to this is: What about drag hounds? Second, the fox will probably die in any case. The best answer to this is: Perhaps it won't. Third, the farmer wants his foxes killed. And I am afraid that this is a cogent reason. Hunting is, after all, not entirely an abstract art. It is done by courtesy of the farmers and with an obligation to them. Too many foxes spared will damage the farmer and, indirectly, the continuance of hunting. But, after all, there is the earth stopper. Cut out the cruelty of digging, and automatically you raise the difficult achievement of one hunting branch: automatically you can congratulate yourself on the artistic ability of your earth-stopper. The whole thing has got a little more difficult, and thus a little more worth while. And with efficient stopping you can surely kill enough of the farmer's foxes, can afford to leave the grounded fox whose strategy has beaten you.

Then there is the quite cruel and facile sport of otter-hunting, conducted in the breeding season so as to save us humans the necessity of paddling in cold water. I should not be sorry to see it abolished altogether, or drastically modified, along with the sport of badger digging. The badger is the last of the English bears. He may do damage in the few districts where his breed is populous, but you need not put him in a bag and release him to the village dogs in an inn yard for that reason. The true badger digger liberates his capture in some other less populated part of the country.

18. i. xxxv.

Sports divide into two main categories: the dangerous and the skilful. I suppose I fly for the former and fish for the latter. Probably some form of *genuine* big-game hunting is the apex of the one, as fishing is of the other. It might be true to say that the best sport is the one that combines the two to the greatest degree, and that this sport may be pig-sticking.

19. i. xxxv.

I am beginning to learn something about training horses, and the more I learn the less orthodox it seems. The first maxim I ever learnt about keeping a horse fit was: 'Give him regular (2 hours) trotting and walking exercise on the roads.' Luke Fieldfare's Laddie never gets anything regular at all, and hunts three days a fortnight at least. Luke gives him his exercise himself. Silver (I am assured by the groom) gets two hours every day, but even one day a week plays him out after a couple of months.

If I had the money to buy a likeable horse, and the time to fuss him in, I should take him out personally for two hours daily. At the start of the season I might walk and trot him for a week or so (during cubbing), but my objective after that would be to give him increasingly more trouble of every sort. We should canter, gallop and jump. What is more, we shouldn't jump the same leaps. Every day it should be half a dozen new fences, or new ways at the same fence. At the end of two months I believe I should have a *fit* horse that was not only as hard as nails, but *clever*.

22. i. xxxv.

One cock pheasant. Carrying him home in triumph, I thought what a pity it was that I knew of no magic charm which could be performed with the aid of his golden mahogany, his blue-sheen on the neck feathers, and his scarlet-circled eye. You can use badger skins to cure consumption, as working in a tanyard does, or smelling peeled oak; moleskin waistcoats, mittens and skull caps, for keeping off the influenza; snake skins for curing headaches; weasel's feet to keep away witches; feathers of a woodcock for paint brushes; but the bright vermilion of a cock pheasant's eye burns only for its own dazzling satisfaction.

23. i. xxxv.

One squirrel, one doe rabbit in milk, one woodcock. 100%, for I only used three cartridges. I don't think a Shire man really needs to be a good shot; for this sort of unexpected scale, from grey tree-rat to 'cock, is the only thing he is likely to encounter. The great shots are the *practised* ones, and I dare say their practice makes for boredom as well as perfection. In the Shire we don't get practice, not the endless reiteration of one kind of mark. A Shire man would shoot a pelican without turning a hair, because his practice is merely alertness for one rare thing after another. I should guess that, on the whole, as an emotional shooter who is not sufficiently particular about the killing range, I expend between two and three cartridges for everything I bring to hand. But if one worked it out mathematically it might be a question of four or five.

26. i. xxxv.

Sinus, 'flu and now a freezing north wind after the hospital ball. Merely a round of visits, with his lordship conducting an increasingly indifferent pack of hounds.

The dull hunting day is rarely recorded in fox-hunting literature, and yet it is not without its charms. It is well to ride a horse with some sort of objective: there is always the stimulating *chance* of sport: the country lays itself open to a discerning eye: and one is out of doors. We were in the woodland to-day, where everything has its peculiarity. Here are a few of the kind of facts, vouched for by sporting writers, that can give food for rumination to even the most disappointed of fox hunters in a woodland country: the small roots of an elm are porous, and are sometimes smoked by plough-boys as cigars; wood pigeons like chestnuts; bees like limes; lime wood slips easily from its bark in the spring, thus providing a good material for making whistles and pop guns; the oak grows, flourishes, and dies in equal periods of three hundred years for each stage; yew berries, like sloes, are nice to eat. Trees, although they look best in isolation, feel *safe* in company. Hence the Wood. Sporting writers are always up-to-date. This is because the country does not change so quickly as the town, and you would need at least the longevity of an oak tree to be out of date in the Shire. To-day I was careful to look at the oak trees, in case there should be a unicorn stuck in them.

Yesterday's hunt took us past the Green, close to the Abbey. All you can see now is what looks like a common barn. Look closely at the gable wall, and you can see a gothic window filled in with wattle and daub: or stone. You can just trace the outlines. Once the nearby Abbey stood on the border of the great Whistlewood Forest. It was surrounded by a moat, a debtor's sanctuary, a flourishing community of monks who died to a man, of plague, in 1346. Then it was a place in private hands, a place where the cattle drank from a trough which was made of an abbot's coffin. Then a farm. Now there is a common barn near it: far from the main road, a deserted green among the fields. Tradition has it that there was a

secret passage between the two. A farmer bored there for a
well. Carved stone came up. 'Put her back,' said the
farmer, 'wheer she come from. T'water be-ant so rareified
as we ull find un somewheers else at um.'

In the old days, when the forest was there, a tenant of the
Abbey was much disturbed by herds of the King's deer,
which used to devastate his vegetable garden. He found it
necessary to keep a watch at night, and the result of his
watch was that one of the buck was observed to have a
human face. The tenant followed the terrible creature in
the blackness of a Shire night, and it led him to a hidden
treasure which made him rich for life.

31. i. xxxv.

At Milton, to finish the partridges. Eight guns killed
about 16 brace, of which I killed 3 brace; of 9 hares I had
one. This is now the third time this season that I have been
invited to the great house, and I am very lucky, for an
ordinary Shire man. If you look at it on the average, it is
few of the average men who get the chance of a big shoot,
even if it is the end of the season. We have to tip, of course,
and as every keeper can tell you it is the poor man who
gives the biggest tip, generally with the best grace. We
don't want to let ourselves be overawed. But it is worth
the tip. When we have worked the whole season for fifty
brace, it is grand to kill fifty brace in a late-season day. It is
lovely to have everything working perfectly; and to draw
for places out of a little silver cylinder; and to move
up two automatically; and to have our choice of whisky,
beer, sloe gin, and cherry brandy; and to feel a warm sort
of affection for the host who treats you so well; and there is
always the shooting, too, the plethora of birds that it
would take ourselves a week to see, and the fact that at
partridges we can shoot as well as the big guns.

1. ii. xxxv.

A name which keeps cropping up in the records round Milton and the north end is Ferrers. I don't think it is the direct line, for the local family name is Grey, but I dare say there is a connection with Lord Ferrers of Groby, in an adjoining county. This latter nobleman was hanged for murder. He asked to be beheaded, after that quietus had gone out of fashion, but yielded to persuasion. They would almost certainly have made a mess of him. He drove to his execution in his own coach, from his own house, with an imposing cortège brought up by his own hearse at the back; and he was hanged in a white silk rope, a curtain cord sent for specially from Groby.

3. ii. xxxv.

The person who travels across the world to see the Indian rope trick might do well to open his eyes nearer home. Wales is stiff with magic. There is a man in my village who talks about witches in the same indignant tone of voice as a colonial uses when he talks about locusts. On the east coast I discovered a village which, within living memory, had chased out all strangers every day at dusk. Anybody not born in that village would be pursued, at nightfall, by a pack of every able-bodied villager, armed with sticks and stones. The result was grievous intermarriage, only about four surnames among all the graves in a big churchyard, and tuberculosis. I was conscious of hostility in the public house in the evening, even in 1933, and felt happier bicycling home. The favourite sport of these people had been known as 'wrastling,' but it had nothing to do with Cumberland and Westmorland. Wrastling took place between two opponents, the toes of whose heavy boots were shod with bone or metal. The objective of the wrastler was to kick his opponent's legs: and the perfect kick was accomplished by waiting until the opponent had lifted one leg to deliver his own blow. At this critical moment you endeavoured to kick the leg which carried his weight, and, if successful, you were usually able to break it.

The publican of a neighbouring village told me that his father hailed from this place, and that he carried a charm around his neck day and night. His legs, from wrastling, were black to the knee when he died. He developed cancer of the tongue, became inarticulate, astonished the doctor by his hold on life. For a week he was unable to speak, or to help himself, or to die. He kept making embryonic movements with his right hand towards his chest. His wife at last realised the purport of the movement, cut the charm from his neck with a pair of scissors, and he died at once.

4. ii. xxxv.

There are few night pleasures to equal the port and starboard lights of an aeroplane, cruising, with a booming noise, across the spaces of the stars. Night has it beauties, to equal the day. The owl glides by, sauntering to its soft-feathered kill: the duck show up against the pricks in the vault of heaven. Even the weather is predictable. If the line between the horns of the crescent moon is vertical to the ground it will be fine: if there is a circle round the moon, you can be sure of rain in twenty-four hours.

5. ii. xxxv.

Now that it seems obvious that this book is going to be published, I am sorry that it is superficial. I am doing nothing because it is my living, but only to amuse myself. Read it beside the good books about the good things, *Farmer's Glory, Corduroy, Morning Tide, Three Fevers, Cobbett*, and it must be a mockery of the real England. It is a gentleman's book. Even if I learn to plough with horses, as I shall, I shall be ploughing for amusement.

To love England properly it is not sufficient to pursue one's sports in her, recognise her trees, cherish her fauna or even drink her beer. You have got to work for her. I do work, a great deal, but in the loveless realms of literature and intelligence. In this sense I can never be a true Englishman. Perhaps I ought to be keeping a diary about the writing of novels, instead of devoting it to my unrealities.

6. ii. xxxv.

I ought to have been a gamekeeper, and have wanted to be, as I have wanted to be a publican or a farmer. It is easy to say that one would like to follow a certain profession when one knows nothing about it; but in this case I am not forgetting the almost wartime vigils of the breeding season, nor the poor pay. All the arts are basically a question of routine. The great artist is in a treadmill, fifty per cent. of his time, even in painting: certainly in literature: also in keeping. But the keeper's is a lovely routine, in and partly because of its rigour.

I am not a keeper, and it is no good saying I should like to be one, because if I really liked I should. Hamlet's is my affliction, between whose desire and reality fell the shadow. I am afraid, among the other fears, of being unemployed.

So this book remains that of a dilettante. When we fixed to publish it, I read *Farmer's Glory* again. It was a humiliating experience, but a stimulating one. A conclusion that emerges, is that my book is that of a person who can afford to be crotchety, whilst his is that of a person who has learned from life. I can afford to deplore the 'going back' of the fields, sentimentally, where he can achieve the greatness of looking forward. It is the difference between life and fantasy.

This going back is a real thing in the north of the Shire. Perhaps it is brought home to me more than to most hunting people, because Silver isn't up to my weight. He is a horse, moreover, who is so sure of his ultimate stability that he can afford to slide carelessly two or three yards on his nose without actually losing his feet. Thus he stumbles over every molehill, teaching me to sit well back and keep on, even with his nose on the ground, and the texture of the field we happen to be hunting over is brought home forcibly. The ridge and furrow of the Duke's country exhausts him if we have to gallop across it. The three hundred guinea hunters pass us without effort, whilst Silver changes feet at every other ridge.

This ridge and furrow (what somebody in *Punch* once called a permanent wave—the only thing I have managed to remember out of *Punch*) is a token of the going back. It shows that these fields were once cultivated, a relic of the former waving wheat. I cannot help feeling sorry for the reaction, not only because Street makes it so obvious that the ploughing was once a beautiful thing, but also because the fields were beautiful under their wheat, and because a peak of human achievement against nature has been reversed. People think it sad when they see a house, that was once lived in, gone to ruin and weeds. The return of the jungle is an emphasis of transience and failure. These fields were once civilised, and now are going back to barbarism.

Street can look forward to dairy farming (and is right), but I can't look back without a sense of having betrayed Tom Scullard.

It will be funny when England is all a factory, when the farms, too, are milk factories, with two hands milking a hundred cows by machinery. We shall lose a texture of the countryside, a change of colour and interest. We shall lose rural employment. We shall lose the stubble for partridges, and the farmhouse of *Farmer's Glory*.

7. ii. xxxv.

Another astounding thing about Street's book is the description of the harvest supper in what he calls the spacious days. It was astounding, because I realised that I had attended three of them. He writes a full description of the supper, given by a farmer, extending over several pages. The description tallies down to the least detail with what I have been attending, these last three years, and attended before in Sussex, as a Village Club Dinner. The food, the songs, the speeches (I have personally made the same speech three times, and am beginning to enjoy it as much as the vocalists enjoy the songs which they repeat as loyally), the toasts, the personnel: all were identical. He might have been describing the club dinner at Renford this year. But there is one difference. Street's dinner was given by the farmer in his own barn ('God Speed the Plough,' was whitewashed on the wall) whilst my dinner is given by the subscriptions of the feasters in the village hall.

One doesn't know how to feel. The pendulum has swung: the world is a machine or a factory. Tom Bourne does not offer a harvest feast, in any case employs only a fraction of his father's men, and enjoys only a pittance of his father's harvest. But the village goes on. Precariously, no longer treated, it insists upon its village feast. We assemble, as we have always done, and make the same speeches, even if it is money out of our own pockets, and the farmer, as a guest, puts ten shillings in the plate which he once filled with cold English ham.

8. ii. xxxv.

I had been proud of the boast that I had not slept in London for five years. Now, with the bother of publishing, I have had to sleep there once or twice. There are two impressive things about the Wen: one, the mourning of the London trees and how they survive; two, the bravery of the people who live there, the town dwellers with their peaky faces and heavy air to breathe, who stand up to its miseries so indomitably.

The London pigeons fly with a special grace, I suppose because of the hard surfaces they have to land on. These surfaces made my feet ache, who can walk in the country for twelve hours on end without noticing it. I looked *up* in Regent's Street, and there were three mallard right above my head. Nobody looks up in London, although air is the only thing which the Wen shares with the country. In St. John's Wood I suddenly realised that at least it was still *called* a wood, which showed that the memory of good things lasts in the deep heart of man, whatever sins he commits with his hands. We cut down trees without bothering much about planting them, and England goes on being de-forested, and perhaps one day the New Forest will be the name of a tube station; but it will be a name still. It is stronger than what we can do to it.

In a fishmonger's there were two salmon. They had been netted, for I could see no gaff marks, but they were salmon all the same. I stood in the hateful smell of the fish shop, and guessed their weight, fourteen and eighteen pounds, and mourned their loss to a Bulldog, and sent my love through the air to Macdonald in the gun-room at this very moment, all on the hard pavement of a street that had once been a wood.

9. ii. xxxv.

Street says somewhere that when he was a boy it was a delight to run down the rabbits which bolted when the corn was being cut, and to kill them with his hands. This, he says, may sound cruel. But of course not. It cannot be easy to run down a loose rabbit. To kill it is an achievement. And if an achievement, a creation: an act over-balancing the death of a rabbit, as I said before.

10. ii. xxxv.

And then the fallacy of leisure. Street makes the point up
to the hilt, but it cannot be made too often. The modern
countryman, and especially the town dweller, who works
certain hours soullessly in order to achieve certain other
hours for the cinema, is not only a bad worker: he is also an
unhappy man. He, now, is sacrificing a part of his day in
order to enjoy the other part. In the old days, as Street
says, he enjoyed the whole day, and took a pride in it. I do
not say this in a spirit of condescension, as from the
intellectual to the bumpkin. My intelligence and leisure
and separation from a pride in my own daily job have
made me personally increasingly more restless and
unhappy.

This is the fallacy at the base of one's intellectual friends,
when they argue for leisure 'to develop the soul.' Fudge.
Street's countrymen developed their souls, before the war,
in their work *as well as* in their leisure.

11. ii. xxxv.

Country grouses, no one gives *them* any publicity
to help in putting them straight. It is a seated evil of the
social system, which seems irremediable without drastic
measures. Fundamentally, the best thing might be a new
war, in which, as quickly as possible, two-thirds of the
population might be wiped out.

For the Wens grow, and suck away the goodness of the
country like boils. The town dwellers think they are the
only people on the earth and commit base (natural)
treachery to the farmers. The farmers are betrayed by
legislation such as that which forced an agricultural wage
without forcing an agricultural price. They are faced with
ruin. Naturally (again) they choose to discharge their
labourers rather than be ruined themselves. And then,
naturally, the labourers are on the streets, pushing prams

which contain all their worldly possessions, bound for unknown and distant poor houses when they have never been out of their own villages, like that man who asked me for a little hoeing four years ago.

I wonder whether the urban population, or their tools the ministers, even prime, realise the condition of their brothers in the country. I know nothing of economics, and my facts are probably wrong, but this is what I glean from conversation in the country parts. It seems that if you are a manufacturer of sparking plugs, or lavatory plugs, or plugs for plugging gangsters in Chicago; you are compelled to arrange for unemployment insurance (called, by us gentry, 'the dole') on the people who do your work. An employee of the plugging, lavatory building, murder creating, machine-working trades, is able to fall back on a monetary reserve if he goes out of employment. There will be something, at any rate, to back him in his motor bicycles and cinemas and cockney squeals. Not so the man whose ancestors have loved, conquered, tamed, and caused the land to yield *food*, since the Battle of Hastings. The country labourer has no unemployment insurance. If he falls out of work he must starve. Or, as an alternative, once he has been (naturally) evicted by his landlord (who has his own living to consider) he may put his belongings into a perambulator and walk to the nearest poor house. I have probably got the name of these institutions wrong; but the point is that in England, at a distance of perhaps twenty miles from each other, there are institutions where a starving man may get his supper and a bed. After (I think) two nights at one of these institutions, the man has got to walk to the next. Whilst he was there he had to do his turn of work (cleaning, peeling, any odd job) and now, after two days, he has got to move on. Whilst he can still walk twenty miles a day he is safe: safe from actual death. We call it, genteely, 'mal-nutrition.' But what about his rights as a man, as a person who has lived and loved and worked in the same village all his life? What about his soul, for which the urban communists claim 'leisure to develop itself in?' What about the man who stopped me on the day of my first solo flight? What about pushing a pram from Warden to Middlehampton?

12. ii. xxxv.

The trouble about books which extol the virtues of England is that they tend to send the wrong people to the wrong places. Some mush-fed maiden nit-lady or gentleman, often even an American or foreigner, thinks that the English countryside must be 'just too grand lovely }.' Off they go to sample the loveliness/grandeur, and fetch up in the Mint House at Pevensey or the bus-fed centres of the English lakes. In the first place it is useless to travel, especially on a main road, and in the second place no self-respecting Englishman would visit the south of England, or Devonshire, or the Lake District.

13. ii. xxxv.

You might travel through England in a motor-car if you liked, simply as reconnaissance. I have found it instructive to drive to Scotland by east and west—on the Great North Road with its intervals of character, or the dingy West Road, through endless suburbs even more tragic by being 'respectable' instead of downright starved—but the drive is only an 'intuitive' survey, like the dilettante's glimpse of a picture by Constable or Crome.

14. ii. xxxv.

It was amusing to go over to Stop to-day, with a party to see the R.A.F. liaison officer, after such a long period of no flying. They had a Siskin there, that had developed a tendency to cut out as soon as throttled back, the same morning. So we were given flights in Tutors.

I have never worn a parachute before. It is a good feeling. They let me pull one in the parachute room before flying, for educational purposes, and the baby parachute, like an Ascot sunshade, popped jack-in-the-box out. It gives confidence to see the thing work. On land one feels an idiot, and rather obscene with the wretched thing bumping one in the knees behind. Not so in the air. And it is not uncomfortable.

After all the boys had gone—they arrived loquacious, were given a couple of stall turns, came down, and sat quite silently in a row—Mouse took me for mine. He said: 'We will go and do some mild aerobatics, if you would like.'

At 2000 ft. he said: 'Would you like to do a slow roll?'

I said: 'I have never done one, but I'm sure I would.'

He said: 'Are you sure you don't mind being upside down?'

I said: 'I don't think I do, but I haven't tried.'

I watched the controls to get an idea, but only at first. We lay over on our off wing, turned upside down. There was no centrifugal force, as in a loop. One simply, slowly, was turned upside down in the air, at 2000 feet, as if one was hanging by a hook from the ceiling. One's bottom was off the seat one was supposed to be sitting on, one's feet were off the rudder bar, one gripped one's harness across the breasts, whilst the blood swelled to one's head, in a homœopathic grip. Slowly the aeroplane turned the right way up. An incredible sensation.

Mouse said: 'How do you like that?'

I said—it was my duty: 'Very much.'

'Would you like to do a loop?'

'Yes, please.'

The nose went down. I watched the A.S.I. 90—100—110—120—130—140. Quite gently, far less dramatically than in the roll, the horizon fell away beneath us. There was an indeterminate moment, and there it was again. A rest cure, nothing to pull one out of the machine.

Mouse said: 'Would you rather do another roll or another loop?'

'Another roll, please.' It was the alternative that my conscious mind wanted. And yet there was a kind of childish thrill about it, a kind of 'I dare.' I think I like rolls. There is one thing about them, and this is that with a parachute one doesn't really worry about falling out. To fall out, pull one's ring (like flushing a lavatory) and be right way up, would be a relief after hanging in one's harness upside down. Or at least, nothing could be more frightening than hanging by one's shoulders; so falling out loses its terrors. I thought almost lovingly about my ring, but gripped the harness none the less, as the machine wallowed thoughtfully over. There was the breath-taking moment for meditation, when all reaction was massacred except a tiny flame of almost insensible fun, and then I was sitting in the seat.

Mouse said: 'Would you like to do a barrel roll?'

'Yes, please.' It couldn't be worse.

It was much better. Quickly, almost with the merciful inholding of the loop, we were round and straight again: an anti-climax.

Mouse said: 'Would you like another loop?'

I said: 'What about a slow roll?'

'You seem to like rolls. We'll do one on the top of a loop.'

The nose went down again, and again the A.S.I. went up: but this time beyond 140, beyond 150, beyond 160, beyond the maximum of the dial. I had always wanted to do that. Down went the horizon, up we went, I pressed from side to side in the cockpit, the harness drew on my shoulder blades, the horizon became ridiculous, repented, turned over, settled itself with an introspective sigh. I was in the seat.

'If you are so fond of rolls,' said Mouse, 'would you like

to do a bit of inverted flying?'

'Yes, please,' said I, but he was trying me high. 'Not for too long,' I added anxiously, now frank at last.

'We can't do it for too long,' said Mouse, 'because of the carburettors. We shall need another 500 feet.'

A Tutor climbs quickly—a treat after what I have been accustomed to—and I had little time to think about my fate.

'Not for too long,' I repeated, at the last moment; and over, slowly, definitely, quite madly, we went.

There was time now to keep an eye on the horizon, to admire the technical brilliance with which he kept his nose just above it, although the world had gone mad. I was gripping my harness with less fervour.

Mouse said: 'What do you think of this?'

'Fine!'

'It's quite easy, really.'

'How many hours have you flown?' I asked, I hope conversationally.

'About 800.'

'I don't believe it's possible.'

(My God, how long is it going on?)

'How on earth do you keep your feet on the rudder?'

'You simply have to press against your shoulders.'

All the time the nose was above the horizon, slightly jerky in its corrections, and the horizon was level with my chin. My head was in it.

'Now we shall have to stop,' said Mouse. With a sigh of relief, but also of a queer reluctance, I was sitting on my parachute again.

'Would you like to take over?'

(I had told him that I had a licence.)

I took the stick gently, with the air-cushioned caress with which I had deflowered my first Moth. It was fine, steady and smooth to fly, a joy ride: seven times easier than the Moth. I had known he would give me the aeroplane, and in the intervals of hanging by my shoulders I had thought: 'Oh, dear, he will expect a demonstration from me, civilian pilots will be in the balance, and I can't do anything at all. Perhaps I had better try a vertical turn.'

But it was eight months since I had flown, and I couldn't fly then.

I turned her into the vertical, tried to hold up her nose. The wind blew on my right cheek. After four or five times round we had lost hundreds of feet. I came out pathetically and began to apologise, shouting into the speaking tube and feeling red in the face. We did two more. The first lost; the second, after a demonstration by Mouse that polished up my recollections, stayed level. Then I put him in a position to land, undershot by a few feet, gave her the engine and left it to him. He properly took her on another circuit, tight, and landed rather cross wind, putting her down with the ease of an absent-minded man putting his pipe in his pocket.

To himself every one is immortal; he may know that he is going to die, but he can never know that he is dead.

SAMUEL BUTLER

15. ii. xxxv.

Another dud Wednesday, with a horrible refusal from Silver, and two Fridays wasted over a press of work. But to-day was not bad.

Almost every sporting writer refers to the nerves of hunting people. It is one of Surtees' pet themes, and now I find that Somerville and Ross make the same kind of reference. According to the latter, six out of every ten people suffer from nerves and two out of those six are in a blue funk. But why don't sporting writers give us their own confessions?

Obviously I was afraid to-day. Silver was never what you might call a safe ride under my weight, except at the start of a season, when dry feeding hadn't had time to wreck him. It was constantly a matter of holding him up, knowing that he would fall over anything between a stone and a rut. Poor devil, he is no longer quite sound in his fore legs. He had begun to look so poor, and go so shaky, that the two weeks' enforced rest came to me with hardly any regret. And I hadn't seen him since the last black Wednesday, and thought of him as the horse he was then. Also it was pouring with rain. At 10.15 I said to the Beam: 'Well, my social position decrees that I should now dress to pursue the fox in a cloudburst. Is it worth it?' I felt this bitterly.

The meet was at Tillerby, and I suppose we must have found at Allthorne. Probably the names are wrong, but never mind. I got a dud, nervous start in the first hunt, and pursued a rear-guard, gate-opening action on the hither side of the brook, to Southwell Mill. I had excused myself to myself by saying: 'I don't want to go to-day and I'm damned if I'll shirk being a coward. So I shall be middle-aged, have a peaceful trot, and see what I can see like that.'

And then, for no apparent cause, unless it was from sheer dislike of the other members of the last line, I can't remember what happened until I was choosing my own places, and smirking at Purcell or Sam Tails, refusing behind me, and feeling a lad. It shows how one warms up. I must have put Silver gingerly at a place, and found he didn't refuse, and tried another, and found him willing if aged, and then I was roaring up a line of horses queueing at a low place, and jumping the high beside them, to the admiration and astonishment of the world. We lost our second fox and ran the third to ground. Then we tried something like Cameron's Gorse, and there was half an hour's wait, and it was cold, and I was soaking, and I was *glad* when we drew blank, so that I could honourably go home at 2.30.

That seems to me to be a perfect gamut. I am not a brave man, but now I am beginning to suspect that nobody else is either. I began sincerely frightened; I spent two short bursts rubbing shoulders with the second flight; I ended with relief. If it hadn't been pouring, if I had owned a horse worth a couple of hundred pound, if it had not been in the Duke's Friday where most of the places are big, perhaps there would have been less of the nerves. But in point of fact I could not deny that I was frightened into impotence during some of the day, any more than I was going joyfully in competition with horses worth five times the price of my own during two happy little scampers, and that I would not have been anywhere else for the world.

Hunting is a queer thing. During the past week I have been a prey to an attack of art, doing hopeless pastels in the studio day and night. It made me think: 'Why on earth do I fly, and fish, and shoot, and hunt, when I am really the sort of person who ought to be leading a depraved life in

Bloomsbury?' There is no answer, except that the sporting life is a compensation. For some reason, probably inefficient teaching, lack of encouragement, and childish neurosis, I was always hopeless at what is called 'Games' at school. Sex probably, the incredibly wicked sex teaching of the grand old manner. So I had to find a compensation. It was my first salmon that made up for a lot of school colours. I don't regret it.

Silver, as a result of his fortnight's rest and regular exercise, was twice the horse he was, and came home fresh. I can't help feeling that if my groom were brilliant at food and exercise, he would have been a good plain horse. Anyway, he is a dear thing. He is never to go to the kennels. When he is too old for use I will put him to grass and let him die of old age, as a gentleman should do. It was pathetic to find him *willing* simply because he was a little fit again, and to know that I had been grousing about him, and even beating him, for being poor.

I find that I have lost the habit of counting fences, which I cultivated assiduously: and though this is a good thing from the point of view of enjoying the hunt in a simple way, I am sorry for the cause of science. The groom who taught me to ride answered my enthusiastic 'How many fences do you have in an average hunt?' with 'Fifty or sixty.' The fact is about two dozen, and then you're going well: I mean for the single horseman in this hunt.

Sam Tails had a fall to-day, but it was behind me and I didn't see.

For me, a happy day: for hunting, only moderate, I suppose. But that seems like life.

16. ii. xxxv.

Mouse is tunnelling in my blood. I got Ker to run me over to Credon, the first time since last summer. It was as if no time had passed at all, although Johnny has gone to be a test pilot, and will never come back any more. The

usual crisis was in full swing. Somebody in a landing
competition had dropped JT in a pancake from feet; thus
presumably winning the competition, but smashing the
undercarriage and a longeron. So JT had gone off by
lorry and another machine had come over from Carlands
to take his place. The new machine was not insured for
solo. This did not worry me. I felt as if I wanted to be
taught all over again, with nothing but dual for years and
years. After the Tutor, I have discovered several things
about a Moth. For one thing, a Moth is by no means easy
to fly well. Her lightness accentuates faults, and a wind
that would be meat and drink to the Avro throws her
about like a hurricane. All those days last summer, when
Johnny said it was too rough to practise landings, would
have been possible for a Tutor. To-day, with a wind that
was not particularly impressive, one was switching off at
400 feet actually over the aerodrome, in order to land on it.
It was a bumpy and tempestuous. I learnt nothing.

Meanwhile Ker had been having the time of his life. It
seems that the master of the Earl's is president of this club,
and he was there in a British Klemm. He took Ker up and
let him fly it (Ker says even land it unaided), an example of
trustfulness with which I should be sorry to compete, if
true. Ker was dancing with excitement, and wanted to buy
a Klemm there and then.

When one is *doing things* one rarely thinks or feels: or at
least not consciously. Fishing is the only thing I can think
of which admits of consciousness, possibly because of the
to-fro moments along the banks, when one is not actually
fishing. Perhaps this is why I have been doing things all
this year. At any rate, to-day I was not conscious. It was
the first day at Credon since last autumn, a day which in
retrospect had its individuality, as every day has. The mere
fact that it had been almost summer for two days: that it
was windy, a strong wind in the air: that it looked like rain
at lunch, but held off, and gave us an April shower just
after we had flown in—one ought to have felt these indi-

vidualities at the time. But no, it was a question of the stick only, the A.S.I., the moment of time and doing in it. Neither hopes nor fears. Action is an opiate, and that is one of the things I have been after.

But looking back from midnight, there were the definite feelings; only observed then as contingent phenomena, now possible to sort out into beauties. The light blur of the sun, and keeping one's nose into it on a tight turn, dazzling before the shower: the *buck* of the Moth after a Tutor: the *attention* to the A.S.I.: the lack of sound—extraordinary, I cannot remember hearing the engine: the *slow* Moth climb: beating back, at half the ground speed, into the wind: the old reservoir, just the same as ever, in the same hack-work circuit: losing the aerodrome for ten seconds: a British Klemm looking as if it were being blown backwards: concentration.

17. ii. xxxv.

I had a curious dream last night, resulting from an argument about the efficiency of the Air Force versus the Royal Navy. Mouse told me a story once about a similar argument between the two forces, as the upshot of which a gyroscopically controlled aeroplane was flown up and down above the Atlantic Fleet for two hours. The entire Fleet blazed away at it, for this space of time, without scoring a hit. Mouse said that the aeroplane was known as the Fairy Queen. I told this story to a boy, who knows a lot about the Navy, and he denied it *in toto*. He said that an up-to-date ship nowadays carries a battery of eight pom-poms grouped together, which fire a shell so delicate as to explode even by hail. A hit with one of these shells, even on a wire or a bit of fabric, would result in an explosion: and the grouping of the pom-poms makes a parallel to a sporting cartridge containing eight shot.

In my dream there was a squadron of aeroplanes, doing the second half of a step-dive upon the ship that I was on.

They were coming at a steep angle, right into the mouths of the guns. It was exquisitely beautiful to see the leading machine directly hit, to see it rear up into the air and explosively disintegrate. I longed for more hits. The second machine sheered up in a loop, without exploding, and the pilot's body fell out, landing with an extended squelch in the field behind my back.

18. ii. xxxv.

I have remembered a fact about my aerobatic with Mouse, which amuses me to put down. When we landed after the rolls and inverted flying, I was hugging myself. It was the obvious case for getting hold of a confidante, and telling him all about it. One wanted to talk continuously for a long time. I was too old to do this. Nobody wanted to hear: they wanted to tell me about themselves. But somebody had to be told, so I told myself. I found an envelope in my pocket, and turned my back upon the audience, and laboriously wrote: 'Two slow rolls; one barrel roll; one loop; one roll on top of loop; one minute inverted flying.' Then I put my paper away, with a hand still trembling with exultation, and listened to somebody's experiences of a stall turn.

I wonder if birds ever go in for aerobatics. Alan swears that he once saw a rook scratch its ear while flying.

19. ii. xxxv.

Scarcely more than two things to-day. Mouse, in a Siskin, doing aerobatics five hundred feet below us. (One kept an anxiously interested eye upon his manœuvres.) And the spectacle of a train.

The first of these two feelings ramifies in more than one direction. (1). A Tutor is not sufficiently devoid of blind spots: one of the ways in which the *modern* aeroplane will develop is this. (2) For some reason I am afraid of aeroplanes underneath me. The inferior blind spot is more difficult to get a peep at than the superior one—for which one can generally bank or wriggle. (3) Aeroplanes are more beautiful as *things* from above, but more beautiful as *movements* from below. (4) Mouse is a grand person. He was doing his stuff for educational purposes and for fun, but obviously *not* to shew off.

The train was the best. For a few seconds there was a red star, like the sun's reflection from a conservatory roof, but strontium coloured. In fact, I was looking down, from 2,500 feet, into the furnace of the boiler. As we came up to the train, and as we began to overtake it, there was nothing special to be seen. But just for those few seconds one was looking directly into the furnace, a door about two feet square, from a height of nearly half a mile.

20. ii. xxxv.

I used to ride a skew-bald pony, with a piggy eye. He was a pony with a strong appreciation of life, which he used to signify, on fine mornings, by making an extraordinary squeak. Eeee, he used to say, and kick out his legs behind.

One evening in my first hunting season, when I knew I was going to hunt next day, I was suddenly filled with glee. I rolled over in bed, with my arms crossed over my chest as if I was going to hug my shoulders, and Eeee came out, exactly like the pony.

I get this feeling now at the beginning of seasons, when it is a question of recollection. You have forgotten the stuffy feathery ball of a dead partridge turning over in the air, or the nuisance of keeping Silver into his bridle so that he will not forge. You think about to-morrow, and suddenly it is there before you in the full colours of life, and the pony's reaction happens of its own accord. Something physical runs down your back.

It happens to me most with fishing. I bought a new rod from Hardy's yesterday, and took it down to the lake to-day, to see if I could remember anything about casts. (I used to fish this lake last year with a trout rod. It is possible to cast a spoon accurately without a spinning reel, by coiling the line in the punt and allowing it to pick itself up. On a trout rod a nine-pound pike—it is *not* particularly difficult to drive the hooks in—is just worth catching. But my trout rod, which had come to no good by this handling, was stolen; and I didn't trouble to buy another. This year I have only fished once, on a borrowed casting rod, and again had a nine-pounder: but it was not worth pulling him out.) To-day I took the new rod down, and cast bitterly into a fierce wind. I was enjoying myself, but only normally, when I remembered the cuckoo.

I heard him last year on the 6th of April. It would be nice to give the feeling. The cuckoo is essentially the Coln in Gloucestershire, a thing mixed up with clear water and cresses. Cuckoo, it said, twice: and there on my fingers was the sticky, the grassy, the fishy smell of trout. There were his rosy stipples, his buck in the hand, the olive dun in the tender nook of his lip. The gut gets in the way as you make to disgorge. He was in my nose and ear and spine.

21. ii. xxxv.

The trouble about life is that there is never time to do anything in it. Painting has been my latest trouble. How is one to hunt, fly, earn one's living, write books, and paint pictures in the one season. Obviously all these things have got to be done, and it is difficult to distinguish between them. Among other things, as Beddoes nearly said, with six years' hard work I might have been a decent painter.

The fascinating thing about painting, when you settle down to learn it technically, is that like all the arts it is *not* accomplished on genius. The 'inspiration' fallacy looks pretty silly when you hand it a paint-box. What has been giving me much honest pleasure, has been the discovery of purely technical tricks, vocational knowledge like not putting two nails in the same grain. Another joy was to find that my first finger lost its skin rubbing pastels, and that my thumb ached at first from holding a palette. In fact, art is a trade. It has its muscles. The sculptor develops a big thumb, just as the roadman develops the small of his back, or the housemaid, I suppose, her knee.

22. ii. xxxv.

One of the best things about the sporting year is the way it fits into itself. You just have long enough at one thing to get accustomed to it, and then the next is upon you with a new surprise. It is an endless procession, a profusion which is sometimes embarrassing. Shooting and hunting seem to get themselves done with a minimum of distracting alternatives, or at least they get themselves begun. In the late winter the alternatives being to perplex. The hunting is still going, and the fish are beginning to run up, and the aeroplanes sound fine.

23. ii. xxxv.

I paid my first genuine visit to an exhibition of paintings. I always had a sort of bogus flair for composition and general aspect. I liked pictures in a way, and generally said the appropriate thing. But to-day I stood enraptured in front of an apparently plain blue background for twenty minutes, examining the paint. It may not have been a particularly good painting, but there was work in it. A genuine person had been carefully scratching and dabbing at the blue (there were the smallest streaks of violet and rose doré in it) with brushes, and penknives, and bits of comb, and heaven knows what else. It was the absorption of trying to identify her *tools*.

Communists have got to be saved, but I think I shall be

able to allow artists into the country straight away. Any trade is a noble one, as Hopkins realised, that has its gear and tackle.

26. ii. xxxv.

I have been going to too many dances, to the extent of using three white waistcoats in a week. There is no excuse for dancing, except sex, and sex dances are not encouraged at hunt balls. If the hunt ball could develop into an African Saturnalia, with all the lady followers doing the shimmy in the centre and the gentlemen riders stamping round the periphery with sexual cries, what a dewy liberation it would be to the psychology of county circles, who all imagine such things upon their secret beds.

An amusing result of leading a double life, between the public-house and the hall, is that one can compare the state of happiness in both places. The county seems universally bored and artificial (oh, the headache after the hunt ball!) whilst the farm labourer seems happy, warm-hearted and alert. Also, of course, much more intelligent.

25. ii. xxxv.

It has been a happy year for me, and I have been a happy man to have it. It is extraordinary to look back over a fine fall in a brook, and a left and right on the first partridge day, and a prize for bad flying, and the first salmon of one's life. It is cold now and the Shire trees are bare: when I began this journal it was cold, but the trees were budding. In between there has been the hay harvest and the bright green leaves of spring, the corn harvest and the death of the trees. They have died, as they are born, in a strict rotation, the oak a conservative last. Foliage goes according to a fixed rule of priority; just as the birds begin to sing, both in the spring of the year and in the morning of every day. Soon the buds will be out again, beginning, if I can remember after all these months, with the chestnut. Soon the money for a salmon river will be twisting my heart again, and the yet more distant piping possibility of a bleached grouse moor in August.

26. ii. xxxv.

We went over to Handley to-day, to see the autogiros, and I was given a flight in one: the pilot being Sedge. There is an urge about these tree-pipit machines which must captivate any moderately sensitive person. Mouse said to me, as we walked to the hangars: 'For God's sake, don't say anything against autogiros. They are all unbalanced about them.' And so they were, but in an infectious way. It is the urge of the pioneer. I have sometimes reproached myself for not being on the surface of the globe in time to come in with the lunacies of Blériot and Grahame White. Here was something remotely comparable; although I was too late to catch the bus, even here. They were people with a mission, people believing in things, touchy and enthusiastic to the last degree. It was a heart-movement of the first magnitude when I said to Sedge in the air: 'What happens if you contrive to turn it upside down?' and he answered: '*Nobody knows.*' If I learned to fly an autogiro next summer would they let me go up with a parachute and try? There was another thing which gave one a proud feeling. Cierva had hawked his invention all over the continent before the British offered him finance. However much we may have been behind the world, however much we may have been apathetic and unpoetical at the birth of aviation, we have snapped into it with this at any rate. The race has its streak of lunacy, its itch for the still vexed Bermoothes.

In the air he said: 'Would you like to have her?' I took the hanging control stick (no rudder bar, except on the ground) by the pure light of instinct. And also, instinctively, I looked at once at the A.S.I. 40! We ought to have stalled. With an agonised mental calculation I decided that by pulling the stick *back*, I should incline the rotors *forward*, and hence drop my nose. It was the wrong calculation, of course. The nose came up and the A.S.I. dropped to 20, or thereabouts. Death was staring me in the face. Well, I thought, the whole thing is obviously insane, so let it take its course.

Slowly it began to get lovely. So far as I can see, nobody can possibly crash this machine, beyond a minor strain. If the worst comes to the worst, you can make a vertical drop at 17 ft. per second. There is no stalling speed.

I have discovered my next spring fever.

27. ii. xxxv.

This is wrong. I love aeroplanes, and can't help going to the window to see them go by: I love the driven partridge and the safe landing, almost always too far back on Silver's quarters, after a big place. But these pleasures are not like fishing, are adulterated. It spoils the true rapture of a hunt if you are partly jumping with fear. I still don't get this off my chest. In the early days, I think I wanted to hunt because I wasn't brave. Now I want to be brave in order to hunt. I want to raise the hounds and the aeroplanes and the pheasants to the purity of the salmon, by cutting out collateral reasons. I fish exclusively for the fishing, and adore it for that: I love the others too, but the love is mixed. They are confused with death and snobbery and desire to excel: all of these, manifestations of fear. And you cannot cast out fear by facing it. So much, at least, has made itself clear. One could go on making parachute jumps for ever, and still be frightened of parachutes. Provided nothing happened. Probably the best thing for a parachutist would be a broken bone: or death itself, the only definite cure for death. I shall stop being frightened of killing myself when I am dead, and then I shall be able to hunt in genuine rapture. But whence the horses?

28. ii. xxxv.

Another fear is the fear of contempt, of other people's
opinion. The people who most assert themselves against
it, most insist upon flouting common standards, are those
who are sensitive to it at heart. I am either a humble or an
arrogant man, if the two things are not the same. If not, I
incline to plump for the former opinion. I was always
agonised at the thought of being not liked, or bullied: and
considered myself suitable for both. It was the humble
hermit crab, stealthily concealing its soft bottom in a
discarded shell, with a shambling motion. All the time I
was at school I can remember this sense of vulnerability; as
if one was in the lions' den, and had to keep the beasts at
bay by an exercise of will. I did so keep them, but only
just. Fancy playing bridge for twelve years and always
being vulnerable.

I wonder whether all little boys believe themselves the
worst in the world. In my case it was a fixed belief, with all
its consequences. I think I must have had a mistaken
mother. When she pleaded so movingly that I should
grow up a big brave and honourable man, she was condi-
tioning me to fear the reverse. I felt myself incapable of
being any of those noble things; and the result was that
whenever anything appeared to be truly noble I found
myself incapable of doing it *ipso facto*. Cricket and rugby
football were, of course, quite the highest things in a boy's
life then, and naturally I was unable to play them. This is
odd and interesting, because there was nothing particularly wrong with my eye. Hockey, for instance, was less
officially noble: and so I was able to play that pretty well. I
could swim to a certain extent, and beat the vicar at tennis,
and shoot straight with luck: but cricket, the Blue Riband
of the Public School (if the term can be spared from the turf
or the latest Atlantic liner) could not be achieved.

One fears contempt, and so lays oneself open to get it. It
was to compensate for rabbiting with the different kinds of

leather ball that I took to a leather saddle. Sport is an escape from games, in a way, an attempt to redress the balance.

This is a bad thing. I allow myself to be chased. It is wrong to hunt so that people can't sneer at one for not playing cricket, even if I hunt for other things as well.

It comes to this, that the only pure sport is fishing. It is the only sport which is pursued entirely for itself. Flying is mixed up with fear of not being brave: hunting, with this and social fears (snobbery): shooting, with fear of the next gun, lest he should wipe your eye and kill a bigger bag—in fact, with fear of failing to excel. But fishing is a secret rapture.

1. iii. xxxv.

A various day. A new burst of foot and mouth put us out of our Friday country, so that hounds met near Milton, near the great shoot. From 15 to 20 miles away, it seemed impossible to get there, until May offered a lift. She was trying a mare from O'Brien's, which had to be boxed over in any case, and it only meant a détour of two miles for the mare's box to pick up Silver. So Silver and I had the rare experience of arriving at a meet like the gentry, the one in a horse-box and the other in a speed twenty Alvis. We made the most of it, and Silver looked well.

There were two hunts to the forest, as far as I can remember after three weeks, both of them quite good fun. A sunshiny day, promising the troubles of spring, and the always fresh pleasure, because decently rare, of leading a field at one's own place just once. I cannot think why jumping is a pleasure. It is not nearly so skilled an occupation as fishing or flying an aeroplane, not in timing, and the danger is small. Perhaps it is a question of sympathy, or rather of trust. One has to, ultimately, trust the horse. I suppose an *observer* in an aeroplane gets the feeling. In the last resort he can't control the pilot any more than the horseman can prevent the hack from falling down. Even the smallest jump is a little act of faith; and thus the pleasure.

May's mare went beautifully, although only over from Ireland the day before. Sending it out looked like an act of madness on the part of O'Brien, but, like an Irishman, he got his reward. She shewed Silver a clean pair of heels, and May was delighted. We knocked off at about half-past two, and talked it over, and May decided to buy. Thus ends a search which has lasted since Christmas, after the trial of innumerable mounts, and with a deep insight into the mentality of copers. It amused me, as a complete idiot over the points of a horse, to spend weeks denigrating capped hocks and sloping pasterns. The great thing is to say nothing, try the horse, and listen to everybody, including the coper.

There was a good fall to-day, at a not important looking gap that I was waiting to get over. Mrs. Bream who rides astride, came a purler: high, wide and handsome. I thought she ought to be concussed; but no, she popped up and apologised like anything to the waiting troop. Silver and I went round another way.

When we had decided to buy the horse, we rang for the box, using Captain Symes' telephone, and there was the lady who came the cropper delivering three or four separate messages over the phone, very competently, I thought, for somebody who looked as if she had been rolled on.

As Jonathan's was near, we drove there for a drink, and found him busy having a divergence of opinion with his wife. Neither of them said anything about this, but Aelfrida looked retained and Jonathan had already taken a little whisky. This was irresistible, to an Irishman who has always been agin the Government, so I set to work to abet him. In half an hour we were on level terms, drawing pictures of each other upside down. I like Jonathan and

Aelfrida very much. We went out and sadly read the epitaph on a shooting dog's grave. Then we came home.

I was feeling cheerful over the sunny weather, and buying the horse, and Jonathan's whisky; so I went out with Ker after tea and shot my top hat with an automatic at fifteen paces. We hit it four or five times, so that now it is not much good as a top hat; but it had never been quite the same since the Southam brook, although it was well worth shooting.

I had a bath, and dressed, and went out for dinner. After dinner we played bridge till two a.m. They gave me a final glass for the road.

I got into the Bentley, waited for the self-starter to die down after failing to engage with the cogs of the flywheel; pressed again, and the engine started beautifully. I was in top gear before the end of the curly drive, with three lovely changes, and driving with happy glee. There was the steep hill to the main road, but my brakes were as good as my engine, and we took it fast. It was a black night. There was, so quick as to be imperceptible, a jolt and leap: I began to brake, but there was no time. Then, immediately, I was forced to rise in my seat. There was the noise of grinding and tearing metal, but much more noise in my own head as it struck the windscreen. An overwhelming flash of light, in a blow so cruel, so pitiless, as to make my inner man exclaim reproachfully. The canals of my throat and nose, inside my head, were full of warm black liquid. Silence and deflation. The night was black.

2. iii. xxxv.

It was the cruelty of the blow that was the interesting part, the thing that made me say 'Oh!' reproachfully to God. It was the difference between hitting one's wife with the flat of one's hand, and hitting her in the mouth with a clenched fist: the difference between fighting with the bare hands and fighting with a poker. To an Englishman's mind there is something wrong about a blow with a poker. It is lawless, dangerous (one might kill and be hanged for it), outside the bounds of sanity, 'below the belt.' But this blow was all those. It was supererogatory, unprincipled, horribly and unnecessarily savage, like kicking a man when he was down. I was unprotected and powerless, but God hit me across the eyes with the poker, and hit me with all his might.

I pushed up my flying goggles with my bloody gauntlets, and started the engine. The headlights had gone out. I managed to back the car, but she would not turn up the hill again. I found that I was bleeding, and that although I had pushed up my goggles I could not see out of my right eye. With my left eye I could see the glow of my tail light. I could not spare time to meddle with the car. I got out of it and walked up the hill in a determined way, with my hands in front of my face, straining with the blind eye to see if I could see the rare faint stars. It was as black as a velvet bag. The other eye was full of blood by the time I reached the drive, so there was nothing to judge position by. I walked into some laurels and a flower-bed. When I found the front door I rang and waited. It was a relief when it opened, and they had not gone to bed.

Felix opened the door and stared at me, but I could not spare the energy to explain. It was obvious. He put his arm round me and urged me up the stairs, which I slowly took. In the bathroom there were May and Patricia and Felix, and I was safe; I fainted.

Everybody was efficient and beautifully kind. It was splendid to rely on other people. I delivered my last words, now that I was back in the bosom of humanity, out of the black night where a star was visible only with one eye: 'Well, this is the end of a perfect day, and at any rate we've got a lovely mare.' The doctor was utterly reliable: you felt he couldn't make it worse, anyway, but he was better than that. He was security. He stitched up the eyelid, swabbed the forehead and the broken nose, bandaged it all up. At four o'clock I went to sleep, propped up in bed, happy and safe. As we thought it more likely than not that I was going to be blind in that eye, it was a matter of interest to find out whether I should.

3. iii. xxxv.

It was a warm pleasure to see with both eyes, and rapture to convalesce; also an opportunity to think in comfort while my brain healed. Death is an interesting thing, and I am beginning to get it clear. Animals are not afraid of dying. They react adversely to pain at the moment before death, but they do not plague themselves about it in advance. Human beings, the weak and pathetic creatures that surround one, and from whom it is our business to rise, frighten themselves by imagining it before it happens. Yeats has it perfect in one of his poems.

> 'Nor dread nor hope attend
> A dying animal.
> A man awaits his end
> Dreading and hoping all.
> Many times he died
> Many times rose again.'

We plague ourselves with the future, which in the present is all imaginary: all unnecessary. The great man in his pride does not anticipate. Death is one of the things that do not repay anticipation.

> 'A great man in his pride,
> Confronting murderous men,
> Casts derision upon
> Suppression of breath.
> He knows death to the bone.
> Man has created death.'

The thing we plague ourselves with is a thing of our own creation. If we do not anticipate it, it is not there. When it comes there, we are not. So we need never meet it.

Death will certainly happen, but that is all. I know that I shall be able to cope with it at its time: and when it is over I am done. I should like it to be a violent death, as no doubt it will be. One finds that at the moment itself there is neither fear nor pity. One seeks to be efficient. I walked up to the Hall without the pain of emotions, merely doing the next thing as well as I could. It would be nice to die like this, functioning. Trying to pull the aeroplane out of its spin (there might be time, although the stall was close to earth), living efficiently, and with concentration, and with interest, to the vanishing moment. The light and the reproachful 'Oh!' would scarcely tax endurance. That being so, why think of it before? Like the animal and the great man, I prefer to live in the present: and not only prefer, but now, after the house wall, am actually contented. It is not necessary to choose. The great man is so.